Wild flowers

Wild flowers

OF SOUTH AFRICA

Approved by the National Botanic Gardens of
South Africa, Kirstenbosch

C. STRUIK PUBLISHERS, CAPE TOWN

PUBLISHER'S NOTE

The Publisher wishes to thank the National Botanic
Gardens of South Africa, Kirstenbosch, and its staff,
especially Dr John Rourke, for their valuable advice and
assistance in the compilation of this book.

We also wish to acknowledge the expert opinions of
Dr B. L. Burtt of Edinburgh and Dr O. M. Hilliard of
Pietermaritzburg regarding the identification of certain of
the plants illustrated.

C. Struik Publishers
Struik House, Oswald Pirow Street, Foreshore, Cape Town

First published as hardcover 1980
Second impression 1983
First published as softcover 1987
Copyright © C. Struik Publishers

Designed by Walther Votteler, Cape Town
Reproduction by Hirt & Carter (Pty) Ltd, Cape Town
Printed and bounded by Tien Wah Press (Pte) Ltd, Singapore

ISBN 0 86977 580 4

CONTENTS

INTRODUCTION

South Africa's floral kingdom — the richest in the world — has been explored by botanists for more than three centuries, yet continues to yield previously unknown species so that the studies begun by men such as Thunberg and Masson continue today. Since the first specimens of South African plants were sent to Europe for identification, more than 18 500 flowering species indigenous to this country have been discovered, though the figure will doubtless prove even higher.

Some are rare, many are prolific, and they range in habitat from the arid wastes of Namaqualand and the Karoo to the lush sub-tropical greenery of the Lowveld, from the dark coastal forests of the Outeniquas to the rugged peaks of the Drakensberg. All have an appeal, whether they are burnished spears of aloes dotting a Transkei hillside, the lordly strelitzias necks proudly craned, the bashful disas or the foul-scented carrion flowers whose pungency attracts the flies which pollinate them.

From this vast botanical treasure-house some 350 of the best-loved species have been chosen for this book. The selection of these has been a daunting task, for to catalogue all our indigenous flowering plants would require 52 further books of a similar size to this — and even then such a 'library' could well be incomplete. It would prove an impossible undertaking both because of the sheer volume of physical work it would involve, and because professional botanists are, as yet, far from completing a descriptive enumeration of all the flora native to our country.

For the botanist, both professional and amateur, this partly uncharted realm provides an exciting challenge and while four-wheel-drive vehicles and modern photographic techniques have replaced the ox-wagons and sketch pads of Thunberg and Masson, many novelties are still to be found and new, undescribed species constantly come to light.

South African botany will continue to present an ever-expanding area of exploration for many years to come but it is clear that, in the forseeable future, a complete guide to all South Africa's wild flowering plants is hardly feasible. At the best one can prise the door ajar and provide a glimpse of part of the incredible wonderland.

The photographs in this book show some of the better known, more colourful plant families that are distinctive of our country. They are arranged in a sequence that approximately follows Engler's systems of classification, with the exception that, as a matter of convenience, the monocotyledons are placed before dicotyledons. In some cases detailed studies or well-illustrated publications are available dealing with certain plant groups which here are covered by only a few photographs. Those seeking further information are referred to the bibliography, whose specialist works would form a useful foundation for a botanical library.

VELD TYPES

In most books on wild flowers, the plants are arranged in taxonomic order, that is in families, with species classified into genera, and genera into families, all arranged in such a manner as to reflect their supposed affinities. However, plant ecologists prefer to study species in distinctive associations or communities, for example in different types of forest, grassland or succulent scrub.

In South Africa the most useful category of plant association is the 'veld type', devised by the late John Acocks, one of the most brilliantly talented botanists this country has produced. He divided, described and mapped the vegetation of southern Africa into 70 veld types, and any enthusiastic naturalist who travels the country by road would gain much pleasure and profit from carrying a copy of Acocks' book with him, and so observe the changing veld types he passes through.

Fynbos, that unique veld type in the South Western Cape mountains, is dominated by families like Ericaceae and Proteaceae, but also contains some endemic families — Bruniaceae and Penaeaceae — which have evolved there and nowhere else in the world. It is best enjoyed on long hikes through the Cedarberg, Hottentots Holland, Klein River, Riviersonderend, Langeberg and Outeniquas. Fynbos has no apparent dormant season — every day of the year something is in bloom. Its special richness is world renowned: moreover, three quarters of its component species are endemic!

Namaqualand, on the other hand, is legendary for

its great spring displays of daisies, but these are brief, often erratic shows, dependent on good regular winter rains. Many visitors to Namaqualand expect to see white, orange or golden fields of *Ursinia, Arctotis, Dimorphotheca* or *Osteospermum*. These large daisy genera are perhaps the backbone of the whole spectacle, but the real delight of that strange wilderness lies in the discovery of countless small plants — bulbous species of the families Iridaceae and Liliaceae — found everywhere among the bushes and koppies, but often unnoticed amid the more blatant massed displays. Namaqualand is best visited from mid-August until late September although, if rains are regular and well-spaced, even October can provide a rewarding show. This is, above all, the place to get out of your car and walk in the veld and, more often than not, get down on your knees! Those who only view Namaqualand from the seats of a car miss its true botanical glory.

The Natal Drakensberg must also be high on any flower-lover's list of places to visit. A summer rainfall region, it is brown, dry and frosted in winter. But summer brings lush green subalpine meadows alive with orchids, bulbs and perennials: and here again one must be on foot to see the best of the flora.

In a very different way the Transvaal Lowveld and Bushveld have great botanical appeal. Here there are areas where South Africa's most magnificent trees are found. Not trees of great stature as in the Knysna forests, but trees with startling forms, brilliant flowers and singular fruits . . . Again, this is an area containing a considerable diversity of species. Indeed, the Kruger National Park should be visited if only to enjoy its marvellous arborescent flora.

Parts of the Southern and Eastern Cape are also well worth visiting, for this area is the meeting place of many diverse veld types often found closely adjacent to each other. The Little Karoo, with its rich succulent flora, is only a few kilometres from the fynbos of the Outeniqua Mountains and the temperate evergreen forests of Knysna, while at the eastern end of the Langkloof, subtropical elements from the Eastern Cape bush start to appear. With Plettenberg Bay as a base, one can see a good cross-section of the country's floral diversity in a single day's drive.

FOLKLORE

South Africa's wild flowers have a scientific as well as an aesthetic appeal. While many wild plants are grown as ornamentals in our gardens — some have even been hybridised, selected and improved — the flora is also of great scientific interest. It is an intellectually stimulating exercise to study the relationships of plant species, how they have evolved, or how their biochemical systems operate.

But to the indigenous peoples of this region the flora is, largely, of utilitarian interest. Wild flowers may be pretty to look at . . . but their roots, berries or bulbs can often be eaten. Arrow poison can be prepared from the latex of others, spells or magic can be encouraged with certain leaves or roots, and there are few plant families that are not used for medicinal purposes.

CONSERVATION

In whatever field lies man's interest in the wild flowers of the sub-continent, it is a sad fact that South Africa's indigenous flora is disappearing at an alarming rate. Farming, urban development and other pressures on land use, each year account for extensive and irreparable destruction. Some veld types are under particularly serious threat, such as the Cape Fynbos where a high proportion of its component species are now regarded as endangered. Fortunately, reserves are proclaimed from time to time and strict conservation legislation is enforced in all provinces, but even these measures can never be wholly successful. Conservation of flora ultimately depends on the public, on local and on individual interest, but can only be promoted by people who are adequately informed.

We hope that this book will open many eyes to the natural wonders on our doorsteps and so help to stimulate and increase an informed interest. Man depends on plant life for his very existence and the more South Africans can be persuaded to grasp this fundamental fact, the better will be their country for future generations.

PHOTOGRAPHERS' ACKNOWLEDGMENT

A. Bannister 1, 7, 36, 136, 186, 273, 294, 334   M. Bayer 158, 165   H. Cameron 88, 384   V. Carruthers 79, 157, 235, 242, 383   S. Chater 16, 19, 38, 51, 55, 92, 115, 194, 244, 245, 248, 265, 297, 340, 397, 402   G. Cubitt 10, 13, 17, 18, 20, 34, 44, 61, 64, 77, 81, 94, 95, 98, 142, 146, 176, 188, 191, 192, 193, 202, 230, 231, 232, 246, 249, 250, 261, 277, 281, 282, 289, 300, 320, 325, 348, 349, 376, 377, 385, 387, 392, 405   D. D'Ewes 33, 330   O. Dose 53, 56   J. Dumoulin 224, 225, 226   S. Eliovsen 40, 86, 253, 371, 390   A. Elliott 163, 169, 205   J. Exelby 219   C. Giddy 5, 9, 12, 21, 22, 24, 28, 48, 76, 78, 172, 187, 190, 195, 222, 228, 229, 241, 279, 284, 313, 324, 333, 344, 351, 357, 372, 380, 386, 396, 400   H. Hall 27, 207, 227   D. Hardy 280, 319   H. Harmer 160, 164, 166, 168, 170, 223   O. Hilliard 363   W. Jackson 2, 41, 66, 68, 126, 128, 143, 155, 171, 173, 179, 204, 220, 267, 268, 272, 274, 275, 276, 295, 298, 304, 305, 306, 307, 338, 342, 353, 364, 393   N. Jacobson 378   E. Lastovica 62, 72, 97, 133, 189, 206, 211, 236, 238, 264, 287, 309, 365, 401, 403   F. le Roux 73, 102, 111, 120   E. Moll 151, 278, 283, 358   J. Morris 26, 32, 288, 315, 346   C. Oberholzer 87   J. Onderstal 11, 15, 99, 100, 101, 141, 156, 239, 243, 255, 262, 263, 285, 290, 360, 361, 362, 373, 379, 381   R. Pearse 23, 35, 43, 50, 59, 65, 85, 257, 404   D. Plowes 31, 54, 75, 80, 91, 131, 134, 135, 139, 148, 200, 251, 258, 260, 310, 321, 322, 323, 326, 327, 328, 332, 335, 336, 337, 339, 367, 368, 369, 370   J. Potgieter 162   E. Rosenstrauch 83, 130, 210, 217, 286, 347, 352, 382   J. Rourke 121, 127, 138, 234   F. Rousseau 103, 105, 106, 118, 119, 122, 123, 124, 329   P. Sargeant 3, 4, 6, 8, 25, 29, 30, 37, 39, 45, 46, 47, 52, 57, 58, 60, 63, 67, 70, 71, 74, 89, 90, 93, 96, 107, 109, 110, 112, 114, 116, 117, 125, 132, 140, 144, 145, 147, 149, 150, 153, 154, 159, 161, 174, 175, 177, 178, 180, 185, 201, 203, 233, 240, 247, 266, 269, 270, 291, 292, 293, 296, 299, 301, 302, 303, 308, 311, 312, 350, 354, 359, 366, 388, 389, 398, 399   L. Stanton 84, 182, 184, 237, 252, 254, 331   D. Steele 108, 213, 259, 318, 374   J. van Jaarsveld 104, 256, 345   U. van der Spuy 14, 42, 69, 129, 152, 183, 208, 209, 317, 343, 396   J. van der Walt 212, 214, 215, 216, 218, 221   H. Vergnani 198   J. Watcham 49, 82, 113, 137, 167, 181, 196, 197, 199, 271, 314, 316, 341, 355, 356, 375, 394, 395.

INDEX

LILIACEAE

The Liliaceae form a large cosmopolitan plant family, very well represented in South Africa where over a thousand species occur, most of them highly ornamental. One of their features is that they are mainly either bulbous or rhizomatous, although succulent and even tree-like forms, as in the aloe, are widespread in this country.

Aloe, with over 140 species in South Africa, is the largest and best-known genus. They grow almost everywhere, brightening winter landscapes, often in brilliant massed displays. The medicinal properties of *Aloe ferox* have been known for a long time and Simon van der Stel found it to be an excellent purgative. Juice tapped from the fleshy leaves is collected, solidified to a crystalline form and still sold under the name 'Cape Aloes'.

However, the Liliaceae are known chiefly for their horticultural importance. *Agapanthus, Kniphofia, Lachenalia* and *Bulbinella* are all South African genera which have been improved and hybridised and are now grown in gardens throughout the world.

Ornithogalum includes not only the famous white-flowered chincherinchee, *O. thyrsoides,* but also yellow and orange-coloured species. Most ornithogalums, of which there are about 60 in South Africa, are extremely poisonous to stock. So too is the famous flame lily, *Gloriosa superba.* This handsome bulbous scrambler occurs naturally in the eastern parts of the country

Aloe microstigma

2. *Daubenya aurea*

and thence up into central Africa. It is found in a range of colou[r] forms, yellow and orange being the most common.

Liliaceae usually have symmetrical or nearly symmetric[al] flowers, but in *Daubenya*, a unique monotypic genus from th[e] Roggeveld, Cape Province, the outermost flowers in eac[h] flowerhead are strongly asymmetrical.

From the simple basic flower structure of this family mar[y] variations have been developed. *Androcymbium* has dull insi[g]nificant flowers made conspicuous by prominent white brac[ts] (modified leaves) that subtend the flowerhead. A differe[nt] strategy is adopted by *Sandersonia aurantiaca*, the scar[ce] Christmas bells of the Natal Midlands, in which the six coloure[d] tepals which make up each flower are no longer free but fused t[o] form a lantern-like bloom.

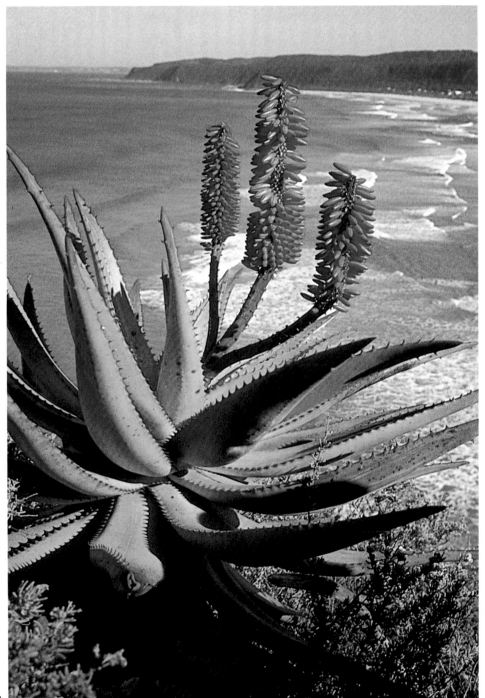

3. *Aloe ferox*: Bitteraalwyn, Tapaalwyn, Goreebosch

4. *Bulbinella floribunda*: Seeroogkatstert

5. *Aloe broomii*: Slangaalwyn, Bergaalwee

Lachenalia sargeantii

7. *Pseudogaltonia clavata:* Gifbol, Groenlelie

8. *Kniphofia praecox:* Red-hot poker

Lachenalia aloides var. *aurea:* Geelklipkalossie, Geelviooltjie

10. *Androcymbium striatum:* Bobbejaanskoen, Patrysblom

11. *Agapanthus inapertus*

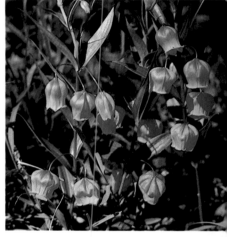

12. *Sandersonia aurantiaca:* Christmas bells, Geelklokki

13. *Gloriosa superba:* Flame lily

4. *Ornithogalum dubium:* Geeltjienkerintjee

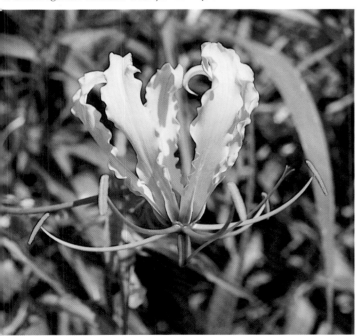

5. *Gloriosa superba:* Flame lily

16. *Agapanthus africanus:* Agapanthus, Bloulelie

AMARYLLIDACEAE

The family Amaryllidaceae occurs all over the world and is comparatively well developed in South Africa, where at least 250 species are found.

Brunsvigia, a genus found mainly in the Cape, clearly demonstrates the umbellate flowerhead in which each flower branches from the same point on the stalk. In autumn, a stout flower-spike emerges from a football-sized bulb, pushes through hard earth, and then unfurls to form a brilliant globe. When it fades, the main stalk separates from the bulb at ground level and tumbles along the ground, scattering seed. Leaves appear later with the first winter rains.

Scadoxus magnificus is a subtropical species from the Eastern Cape, Natal and the Transvaal. *Ammocharis coranica*, frequent in the summer rainfall area, often forms massed displays. In Lesotho, a gluey paste made from cooked *Ammocharis* bulbs is used to mend cracks in clay pots.

There are only four species of *Clivia*, all of them endemic to South Africa. *C. miniata* from the forests of Natal has been a garden favourite for over a century. The common orange form is shown here, but the rare clear yellow is also sometimes seen.

Crinums are among the most robust South African amaryllids, occasionally producing flower-spikes over a metre high. More modest is *Crinum campanulatum,* an unusual aquatic species often seen growing partly submerged in Eastern Cape vleis.

Cyrtanthus is another large genus. Several species are popular-

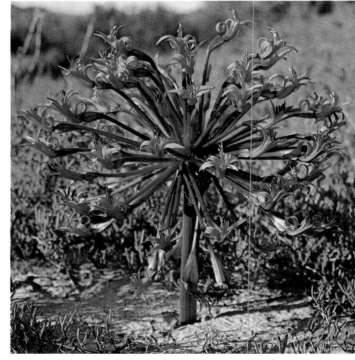

18. *Brunsvigia orientalis:* Candelabra flower, Konings-kandelaarblom

19. *Brunsvigia marginata*

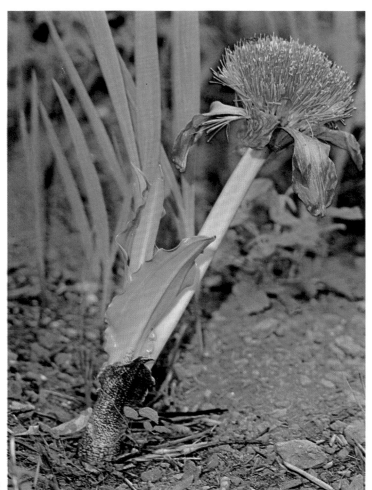

17. *Scadoxus puniceus:* Paintbrush, Poeierkwas

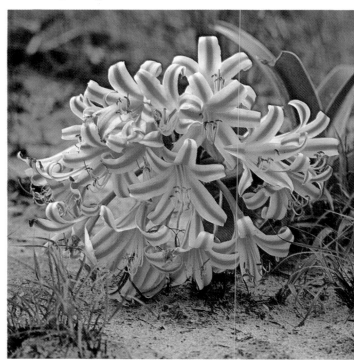

20. *Ammocharis coranica:* Gifbol, Seeroogblom

. *Clivia miniata:* Bush lily, Boslelie

22. *Crinum campanulatum:* Vleilelie

23. *Cyrtanthus breviflorus*

ly called fire lilies because of their habit of bursting into flower after a veld fire. This is especially true of the Western Cape species, *C. ventricosus,* frequently seen a fortnight after the veld has been destroyed by fire, illuminating an ashen landscape.

In its natural state, *Amaryllis belladona,* the March lily, responds similarly to fire, but tends to bloom more regularly when cultivated.

Kukumakranka is the popular name for *Gethyllis,* of which there are a dozen species in the Western Cape and Namaqualand. The delicately perfumed flowers are followed in late autumn by deliciously aromatic cylindrical fruits, used by farmers to flavour liqueur brandy.

Many other amaryllids have fleshy fruits, especially obvious in *Haemanthus,* where the flowers precede shiny crimson berries.

Boophane disticha, the 'gifbol', is used by indigenous people of South Africa to poison their arrows. Like *Brunsvigia,* its spent heads tumble about in the wind dispersing their seeds.

Nerine, a genus of some 30 species, is one of South Africa's greatest contributions to the world's gardens. Most hybrids have the Western Cape *N. sarniensis* in their parentage.

24. *Cyrtanthus contractus:* Fire lily, Vuurlelie

25. *Cyrtanthus ventricosus:* Brandlelie

5. *Amaryllis belladona:* Belladonna lily, Belladonnalelie

27. *Gethyllis britteniana:* Kukumakranka, Koekoemakranka

3. *Clivia nobilis:* Bush lily, Boslelie

29. *Haemanthus rotundifolius:* April-fool, Velskoenblaar

30. *Haemanthus rotundifolius*

31. *Brunsvigia gregaria*

32. *Cyrtanthus sanguineus:* Ifafa lily, Keilelie

33. *Cybistetes longifolia:* Malagash lily, Malgaslelie

34. *Apodolirion ettae*

5. *Boophane disticha:* Poison bulb, Seeroogblom

36. *Boophane disticha:* Poison bulb, Seeroogblom

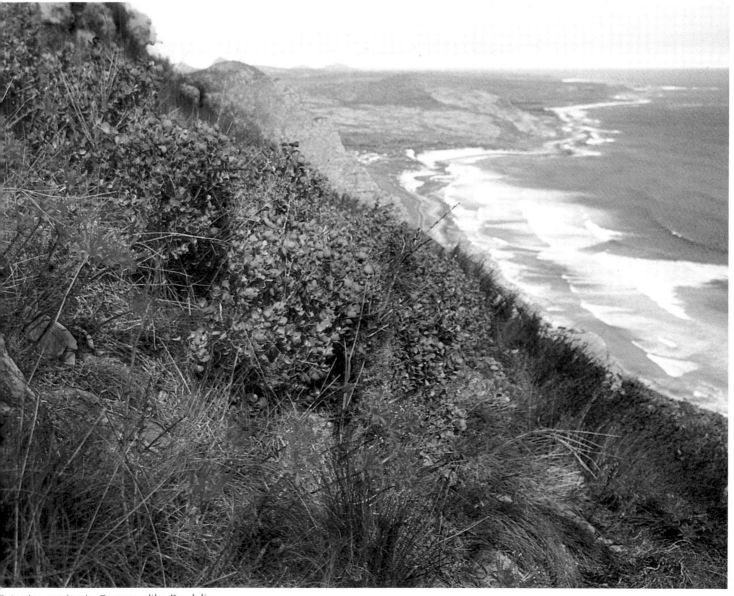

. *Nerine sarniensis:* Guernsey lily, Berglelie

HAEMODORACEAE

38. *Wachendorfia thyrsiflora:* Rooikanol

The root systems of plants seldom possess characters which can be used as an aid to identification at family level. However, in the Haemodoraceae or blood-root family, both the rhizomatous and cormous rootstocks, at least in the South African species, all contain brilliant orange-red pigments. This small family is best developed in countries of the Southern Hemisphere and is represented in South Africa by about 20 species. *Dilatris* and *Wachendorfia* are the largest genera.

Wachendorfia thyrsiflora, a spectacular streamside plant from the Western Cape mountains, has prominently pleated leaves and produces two-metre-tall yellow flower-spikes in springtime. *Dilatris corymbosa* tends to appear in drier mountain areas of the Western Cape, while *D. viscosa* is only found in permanently moist areas on the higher peaks.

39. *Dilatris corymbosa:* Rooiwortel

40. *Wachendorfia thyrsiflora:* Rooikanol

41. *Dilatris viscosa*

APONOGETONACEAE

This exclusively aquatic family consists of a single genus, *Aponogeton,* which is found mainly in Africa, Madagascar and Australia. Of the 25 species, five occur in South Africa, the best-known species being *A. distachyos,* the 'waterblommetjie' or 'wateruintjie'. White, bilobed, sweetly scented flowerheads appear in late winter and spring, floating among the leaves on Cape vleis, or other shallow expanses of water. The mature flower-heads are the major ingredient in a highly esteemed traditional dish, waterblommetjiebredie (a stew of mutton and waterblommetjies). Demand is so great that the blooms are now canned commercially and some farmers are even cultivating them in artificial ponds.

As natural vleis dry up in summer the plants die back to resting subterranean rhizomes until the winter rains begin, when they sprout again to start a new growth cycle.

A. distachyos, being an interesting aquatic, has long been cultivated abroad as the Cape water hawthorn.

42. *Aponogeton distachyos:* Cape pondweed, Waterblommetjie

VELLOZIACEAE

In South Africa this small tropical to subtropical family comprises only two genera, *Xerophyta* and *Talbotia. Xerophyta* is the largest and most conspicuous genus with about six species found in the Transvaal, Swaziland and Natal. Several, like *Xerophyta viscosa,* are tall-stemmed. The strange growth habit of these plants at once attracts attention: they appear as blackened clumps covered by hard fibrous layers with tufts of coarse, grass-like leaves at the tip of each stem. In spring these apparently dead stumps come to life as delicate mauve blooms appear from their tips. Xerophytas are generally found in and around rocky habitats. They survive frequent burning and may grow to anything from a metre to three metres in height. In the Transvaal they are usually called 'bobbejaanstert' or black-stick lilies.

. *Xerophyta viscosa*

44. *Xerophyta viscosa*

HYPOXIDACEAE

Some botanists classify members of this family among the Amaryllidaceae but, especially in South Africa, they form a very distinct group. The family is largely confined to the southern hemisphere and comprises approximately 130 species in eight genera. Over half that number of species, grouped in five genera, is found in South Africa which clearly suggests that the Hypoxidaceae has undergone considerable evolutionary diversification in this region. All our hypoxids are geophytes, i.e. they survive the dry season with corms or rhizomatous rootstocks. *Hypoxis* itself is a rather nondescript genus of yellow-flowered herbaceous species found mainly in the Transvaal and Natal grassveld.

But *Spiloxene* is the most beguiling genus of some 30 species dispersed throughout the South-Western Cape where they are commonly called 'sterretjies': the two peacock-eyed *Spiloxenes*, *S. capensis* and *S. canaliculata*, are the ones most admired. They appear in damp fields or along ditches and seepage areas, flowering in spring and often growing together. *S. capensis* may be plain yellow or white, or white or pink with a peacock-eye at the centre. The eye is formed from patches of black purple or iridescent green at the base of each petal. *S. canaliculata* also has an eye, but is usually orange or yellow.

Equally charming but seldom seen is *Rhodohypoxis baurii*, one of the gems of the high Drakensberg. Its tolerance of severe frost has made this exquisite miniature a favourite with alpine gardeners in Britain. The petal colour covers a wide range, from pure white to deep burgundy, but is most commonly a shade of pink.

45. *Spiloxene curculigoides:* Sterretjie

46. *Spiloxene canaliculata:* Geelsterretjie

47. *Spiloxene capensis:* Golden star, Geelsterretjie

B. *Rhodohypoxis baurii:* Rooisterretjie

9. *Spiloxene capensis:* Golden star, Geelsterretjie

50. *Rhodohypoxis baurii:* Rooisterretjie

IRIDACEAE

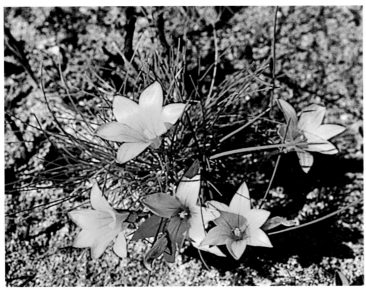

51. *Romulea flava*: Frutang, Froetang

52. *Babiana rubrocyanea*: Kelkiewyn

The Iris family is cosmopolitan in its distribution and comprises some 1 500 species, but in South Africa it is probably better developed than elsewhere. Over 860 species are found here — more than half the world total for the family. By far the greatest majority occur in the South Western Cape and Namaqualand. *Gladiolus,* with about 105 species, is our largest genus.

Over the past two centuries many South African irids have been domesticated and are now familiar garden plants, such as gladioli, freesias, crocosmias, ixias and watsonias. Some have been so 'improved' by plant breeders that often it is not easy to associate modern garden hybrids with their humble wild ancestors in the veld.

Most of the Cape genera are deciduous, sprouting from underground corms with the advent of the wet season, flowering, and then dying back and becoming dormant during the dry season. *Moraea, Hesperantha, Romulea, Geissorhiza, Homoglossum, Gladiolus* and *Babiana* are among the larger genera which are common in the Western Cape, flowering in autumn, winter and spring.

Watsonia is one of the more robust and is dispersed throughout the country. Several species are evergreen and most tend to flower profusely after veld fires. In fact, certain watsonias such as *W. comptonii* will only flower after burning and actually need a veld fire to initiate the flowering process.

Nivenia and *Witsenia* are unique in that they have a shrubby growth habit with woody stems, lacking any underground corms or rhizomes. Both are found only in the mountains of the Western Cape.

In Natal and the Transvaal, clumps of *Dierama,* sometimes called hairbells, are seen in moist grassveld, while at higher elevations in these areas pink or red *Schizostylis* brighten the margins of mountain streams. Both are frequently cultivated, as are the handsome *Dietes* from the Eastern Cape and Natal.

32 Flowers in the Iridaceae family come in every known colour and

53. *Hesperantha vaginata*

. *Babiana villosa:* Rooibobbejaantjie

. *Nivenia stokoei*

56. *Moraea tricolor*

57. *Watsonia comptonii*

58. *Watsonia tabularis*

59. *Schizostylis coccinea:* Kaffir lily, Kafferlelie

60. *Aristea spiralis*

34

Dierama pictum

62. Geissorhiza ovata

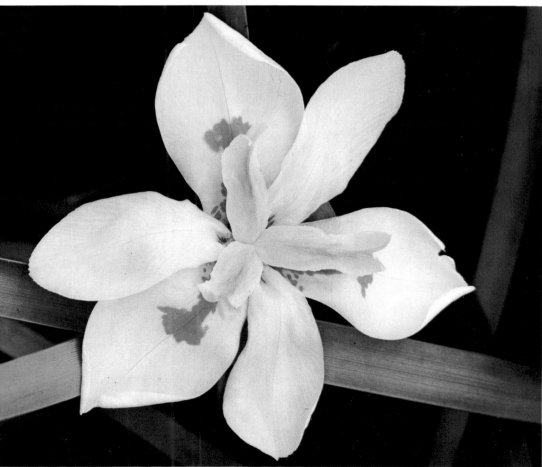

Homoglossum merianellum:
mes, Rooi-afrikaner

64. Dietes grandiflora

35

65. *Crocosmia aurea*

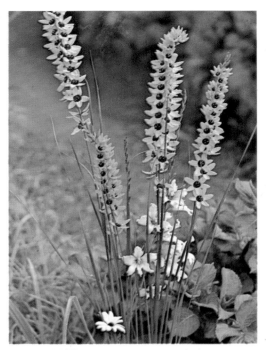

66. *Ixia viridiflora:* Green ixia, Groenkalossie

67. *Gladiolus cardinalis:*
Waterfall gladiolus, Nuwejaarsafrikaner

68. *Gladiolus maculatus:* Aandblom

colour combination. Some are almost transparent, such
Gladiolus hyalinus, but the most astonishing is the turquoi
green *Ixia viridiflora* from Tulbagh in the Cape. Other gene
such as *Hesperantha* open towards evening while certa
moraeas and aristeas have such delicate ephemeral petals th
after opening for a few hours they wither away.

Iridaceae are of little economic value but of considerab
horticultural importance. *Moraea polystachya* and seve
species of *Homeria* are poisonous to man and beast, but t
majority of other genera have edible corms. These were consu
ed by primitive man, and even today in remote country distric
especially Namaqualand, irid corms, or 'uintjies', are gather
and eaten, raw or roasted.

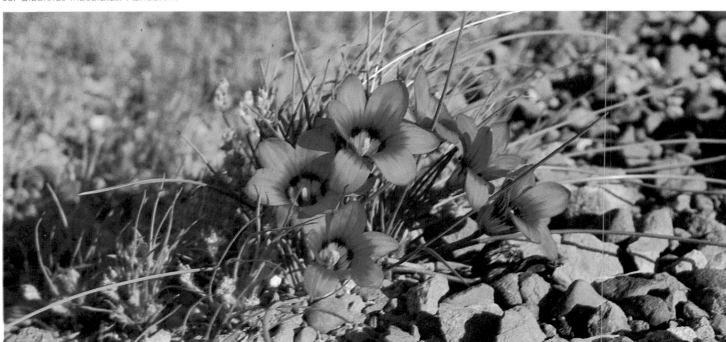

69. *Romulea rosea:* Frutang, Froetang

. *Gladiolus hyalinus:* Kliplelie, Klippypie

71. *Gladiolus maculatus:* Aandblom

. *Gladiolus alatus:* Kalkoentjie

73. *Anapalina caffra*

74. *Witsenia maura:* Bokmakieriestert

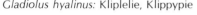

37

POACEAE

Grasses, so rarely illustrated in books on wild flowers, belong to a huge cosmopolitan family, the Poaceae (also known as Gramineae). Approximately 9 000 species are dispersed over the globe from the fringes of the polar wastes to the equator. They can be said to be the most important plants on earth for they provide man with such essentials as cereals, sugar and grazing for his stock: ubiquitous but easily overlooked. In South Africa about 750 species have been recorded, forming much of the plant cover in summer rainfall areas. *Rhynchelytrum repens,* red-top grass, is perhaps the most beautiful of our grasses. Originally from Natal and the Transvaal, it is now naturalised in parts of the Western Cape.

75. *Rhynchelytrum repens:* Natal red-top, Bergrooigras

76. *Jubaeopsis caffra:*
Pondoland coconut, Palmboom

77. *Hyphaene natalensis:* Ilala palm

78. *Raphia australis:* Raphia palm

ARECACEAE (PALMAE)

Palms are essentially tropical or subtropical trees and belong to a large pa tropical family. Only five species are indigenous to South Africa and all gro in the warmer parts of the country. The most unusual is the mkambati palr *Jubaeopsis caffra,* only found at three localities along the Transkei coa *Hyphaene ventricosa* is perhaps the most typical of our palms, often seen the Kruger National Park. *Raphia australis* from the Zululand coast is monocarpic (fruiting once only) species taking years to grow to maturity: ar then it flowers once and dies.

The Raphia palm's strong leaf midribs are used by black people for buildir huts as well as their traditional rafts that are still used on the Kosi lake syste of northern Zululand.

STRELITZIACEAE

Only five species represent this small pan-tropical family in South Africa, but all are handsome, producing most arresting flowers and leaves.

Strelitzia reginae, the crane flower, is herbaceous. It grows up to two metres high in its natural habitat, the Eastern Cape coastal bush, and it is cultivated by commercial growers in most warm countries for its magnificent orange, blue and white blooms: pale yellow mutants are occasionally seen. The white and blue flowered species are trees up to ten metres high with enormous stalked leaves. *S. alba* (Knysna to Humansdorp) and *S. nicolai* (East London to Natal) are found in coastal areas, to which they give a distinctly exotic tropical atmosphere, while *S. caudata,* similar in appearance, grows only in the Northern Transvaal.

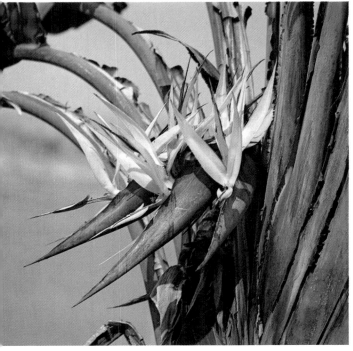

. *Strelitzia nicolai:* Natal strelitzia

80. *Strelitzia nicolai:* Natal strelitzia

. *Strelitzia reginae:* Bird of Paradise flower, Wildepiesang

ARACEAE

Most aroids grow in the tropics or subtropics, but a number do occur in temperate regions where they usually become deciduous and are either bulbous or rhizomatous.

Zantedeschia is an exclusively South African genus of six species, popularly known as arum lilies. Each 'flower' is in fact a composite structure consisting of a coloured spathe or sheathing bract enclosing a finger-like spadix, a fleshy spine bearing hundreds of minute, individual flowers. *Z. aethiopica,* the commonest species, is white and has become almost a weed in its native Western Cape, adorning ditches, vleis and streamsides from early winter to late spring. Forms of this species with greenish spathes are occasionally seen. In the Transvaal grow the yellow-flowered *Z. pentlandii,* the tiny pink-flowered *Z. rehmannii* and the cream-coloured *Z. albomaculata* with its spotted leaves.

82. *Zantedeschia aethiopica* (form): Arum lily, Varklelie

83. *Zantedeschia aethiopica:* Arum lily, Varklelie

. *Zantedeschia pentlandii*

85. *Zantedeschia albomaculata:* Kleinvarkblom

86. *Zantedeschia pentlandii*

87. *Zantedeschia rehmannii:* Purple arum, Persvarkblom

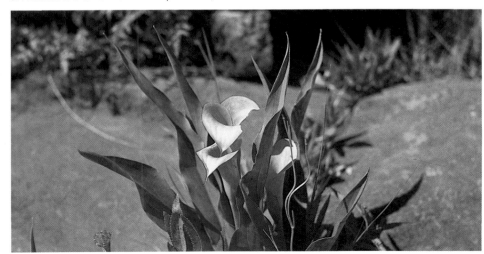

88. *Zantedeschia rehmannii:* Purple arum, Persvarkblom

41

ORCHIDACEAE

Orchids form one of the largest families of plants in the world, some 18 000 species in all, of which about 550 grow wild in South Africa. They are highly prized for their spectacular flowers, especially those of tropical epiphytic species (i.e. growing on another plant but not parasitic).

Ansellia gigantea is the largest of our epiphytic orchids. It is occasionally seen flowering in the crowns of bushveld trees in the Transvaal Lowveld and in Zululand.

However, most South African orchids are terrestrial or ground dwelling species such as *Disa* (70 species) and *Satyrium* (45 species), our largest genera. The famous red disa, *D. uniflora,* which grows beside streams and waterfalls in the Western Cape mountains, is probably the most magnificent red-flowered orchid known. *Orthopenthea, Disperis, Herschelia, Penthea* and *Ceratandra* are all genera from the high Cape mountains. Like many other bulbous or tuberous plants in the Cape, they tend to be stimulated to flower by burning, often flowering profusely after a veld fire only to 'disappear' until the next one stimulates them to bloom again.

Bartholina burmanniana, a tiny, delicate species with a deeply incised lower lip, is commonly called the spider orchid. It tends to grow concealed under bushes, where it is easily overlooked but is found on heavy clay soils in many parts of the Western Cape, flowering in spring.

89. *Disperis capensis:* Granny-bonnet, Moederkappie

90. *Herschelia graminifolia:* Blue Disa, Bloumoederkappie

91. *Bartholina burmanniana:* Spider orchid, Spinnekopblom

92. *Disa glandulosa*

93. *Disa uniflora:* Pride of Table Mountain, Rooidisa

4. *Ceratandra grandiflora*

95. *Penthea filicornis*

. *Orthopenthea atricapilla*

97. *Satyrium coriifolia:* Ewwa-trewwa

43

44

98. *Ansellia gigantea:* Tiger orchid

MORACEAE

This is the family to which figs and mulberries belong. *Ficus* — the figs — is the largest genus, containing over 1 000 species distributed over most of the warmer regions of the world. In South Africa there are about 25 species of *Ficus* all producing edible though rather dry, insipid fruits. The fig fruit itself is actually a collection of hundreds of tiny flowers arranged inside a globe-like structure with a distinct pore or opening at one end. When fully developed the pore opens to admit tiny, highly specialized flies which crawl inside and pollinate the individual flowers. Apart from their characteristic fruits (figs), all *Ficus* species exude a white milky latex when a stem or leaf stalk is snapped. *Ficus capensis,* the Cape fig, is our most widespread species, ranging from the Southern Cape to the Transvaal; it is also probably our most beautiful, producing long pendulous trusses of bright pink figs from its main branches. Most figs are exceptionally handsome trees, especially *F. sansibarica* which can be seen in many parts of the Transvaal Lowveld. This species may become a strangler, starting life as a seedling in a branch cleft on a host tree, eventually putting out aerial roots, and ultimately enveloping and later strangling the host species on which it originally germinated. *Ficus sonderi* is also equipped with powerful roots but is a rock-splitter rather than a strangler. Here a seed sometimes germinates in a rock crevice, forcing the rocks asunder as the roots grow and mature, snaking their way between exposed fissure lines.

99. *Ficus capensis:* Cape fig

100. *Ficus sonderi:* Mountain rock fig

101. *Ficus sansibarica:* Zanzibar fig

PROTEACEAE

South Africa and Australia are the two most important centres of distribution for this characteristically Southern Hemisphere family. About 450 species are found in South Africa where *Protea* (82 species), *Leucadendron* (82 species) and *Leucospermum* (48 species) are the largest genera. Most of the family is concentrated in the South Western Cape where proteaceous plants make up an important broad-leaved shrubby component of fynbos vegetation. *Protea cynaroides*, a widely-dispersed species from mountainous country between Citrusdal and Grahamstown

102. *Mimetes cucullatus:* Rooistompie

is South Africa's national flower with flowerheads up to 30 cm in diameter. Proteas are named after the Greek god Proteus, who had the ability to change his shape, and take on many forms. Some are trees (*P. glabra*), or shrubs (*P. neriifolia*) while others have a low tufted growth habit as in *P. cryophila*, the snow protea from the high Cedarberg Mountains. Most brightly coloured shrubby species are pol-

103. *Mimetes hirtus*

104. *Protea cynaroides:* Giant protea

106. *Leucospermum reflexum*

107. *Protea compacta*

105. *Leucospermum glabrum:* George pincushion

108. *Protea cynaroides:* Giant protea

9. *Protea glabra*   110. *Protea stokoei:* Stokoe's protea   111. *Protea neriifolia:* Blousuikerbos   112. *Protea lorifolia*

3. *Leucospermum cordifolium:* Pincushion

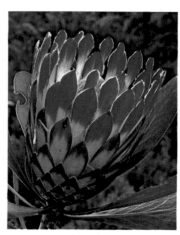

4. *Protea aurea*   115. *Leucadendron tinctum* (female)   116. *Mimetes hottentoticus:* Matchstick mimetes   117. *Protea obtusifolia:* Bredasdorp protea

47

118. *Leucadendron salignum:* Tolbos

119. *Serruria florida:* Blushing bride

120. *Leucospermum tottum*

linated by the Cape sugarbird, seen here on *P. cynaroides.* Suga
birds feed both on nectar and tiny insects in the flowerheads

Several different natural evolutionary strategies have bee
adopted to produce brilliant flowerheads in this family. Bright
coloured leaves called bracts surround each flowerhead in *Pr
tea,* but in *Leucospermum* (pincushions) and *Mimetes* it is the cc
ourful styles that create a show. *Leucadendron* (geelbos) h
male and female flowers on different plants, the females bei
massed in woody cones; *Paranomus* and *Serruria* rely on bo
styles and perianths to produce their display; *Serruria florida,* t
blushing bride, is a rare species in its natural habitat
Assegaaibos in the French Hoek Mountains, but its horticultur
popularity has happily ensured its security as a species.

48

121. *Protea cryophila:* Snow protea

122. *Leucadendron laureolum:* Geelbos

3. *Leucadendron conicum*

125. *Serruria vallaris*

126. *Leucospermum calligerum*

4. *Leucadendron linifolium*

127. *Leucospermum truncatum*

128. *Leucadendron spissifolium:* Vleitolbos

49

MESEMBRYANTHEMACEAE

Vygies (little figs), is a popular name for many members of the great pan-tropical family which is centred in South Africa where over 2 000 species are found and where climate variations have caused the Mesembryanthemaceae numerous diversities as they adapted to conditions of great aridity and in so doing evolving some bizarre growth forms. The greatest species concentrations are found in Namaqualand, the North Western Cape and Little Karoo. Mesembryanthemum means midday flower and denotes its habit of opening towards midday in warm sunny weather, and closing on dull days and at night. All are succulents but the degree of fleshiness varies from genus to genus. *Lampranthus* are generally shrubby: *L. roseus* in pink, white and red colour forms and the yellow *L. aureus* are two of our most widely cultivated vygies. At the other extreme are dwarf genera such as *Conophytum, Pleiospilos* and *Lithops,* which have one or more spherical 'bodies', each composed of a pair of fused leaves.

Sometimes an adult plant is reduced to a single pair of leaves in *Lithops,* the stone plants. Mimicry is an important feature these genera, particularly in *Conophytum* whose speckled bodi often resemble the lichenous encrustations on rocks in who cracks and crevices it is to be found, while *Lithops* matches t colour and even the texture of the stones and rocks among which it grows so successfully that it often escapes detection I hungry animals.

Fenestraria — the name means a collection of windows — even more remarkable. Here whole plants are buried in loo sand which protects them from blistering heat and inten sunlight. Only the tops of the cylindrical leaves emerge, their ti being provided with lens-like 'windows' admitting just sufficie light to sustain photosynthesis. These astonishing 'window-plan grow in the southern Namib Desert and at the Orange Riv mouth.

129. *Lampranthus roseus:* Red vygie

130. *Lampranthus aureus:* Golden vygie

131. *Fenestraria rhopalophylla*

132. *Lampranthus watermeyeri*

133. *Pleiospilos nelii:* Kwaggavygie

134. *Conophytum pellucidum*

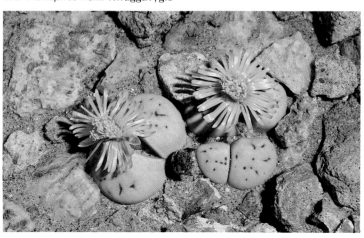

135. *Lithops ruschiorum:* Stone plant

51

137. *Drosanthemum speciosum*

136. *Carpobrotus quadrifidus*

138. *Dorotheanthus rourkei*

139. *Dorotheanthus bellidiformis:* Bokbaaivygie

Conicosia and Carpobrotus are trailing perennials. In Carpobrotus, soft edible fruits containing an acid pulp appear a few weeks after the dazzling flowers have faded. These are gathered and sold as 'sour figs'. Dorotheanthus is a genus of succulent annuals; D. bellidiformis, the famous Bokbaaivygie, grows wild along the Cape West Coast between Milnerton and Saldanha, and is a great spring favourite in gardens the world over; D. rourkei, a rare Namaqualand species, has hitherto defied attempts to cultivate it.

40. *Conicosia pugioniformis:* Varkslaai

LORANTHACEAE

About 50 species of this essentially tropical to subtropical family — popularly called mistletoes — are found in South Africa. All are parasites, growing on other trees or shrubs: but only partial parasites, drawing water and nutrients from their hosts but producing carbohydrates from their own green stems and leaves. *Viscum* (true mistletoe) accounts for about half the local species while the remainder are placed in various other genera.

Loranthus and *Tapinanthus* are especially colourful when in bloom, so much so that many an apparently floriferous tree on closer inspection often turns out to be heavily infested with *Loranthus* or *Tapinanthus* in full bloom! *Tapinanthus rubromarginatus* is common in the Transvaal, usually on *Acacia* trees.

The flowers are followed by sticky, edible berries on which birds feed and which stick to their beaks and are then wiped off on the branches of another host, where the seeds soon germinate, putting out a strong root which bores into the vascular tissue of the host tree, thus starting a new life cycle.

141. *Tapinanthus rubromarginatus*

AMARANTHACEAE

This rather unprepossessing, pan-tropical family has the dubious distinction of counting many troublesome agricultural weeds among its ranks. However, a few garden plants, for example *Celosia* (cockscomb), also belong here. It is rather well represented in South Africa, especially in the arid western and central regions of the country where annual and herbaceous species flourish on the meagre rainfall of occasional summer thundershowers. *Hermbstaedtia odorata* shows the family's typical feature, namely, tiny massed flowerheads with each flower surrounded by dry, chaffy coloured bracts.

142. *Hermbstaedtia odorata*: Katstert

RANUNCULACEAE

Although centred mainly in cool temperate parts of the Northern Hemisphere, the Ranunculus family does have about 25 species indigenous to South Africa, mainly in the genus *Knowltonia*. A rhizomatous perennial, common in coastal bush and forested koofs, *Knowltonia capensis* is a very handsome green-flowered species.

Anemone tenuifolia is an evergreen perennial from the higher Cape mountains. It flowers rather erratically under normal conditions but blooms profusely after veld fires making a splendid show in white, pink or cerise. Traveller's joy is the common name for *Clematis brachiata,* a rampant, sweetly scented climber which festoons both bush and forest margins in the Cape, Transvaal and Natal during December and January.

144. *Knowltonia capensis:* Katjieblaar

143. *Clematis brachiata:* Traveller's joy, Klimop

145. *Anemone tenuifolia:* Anemone, Syblom

NYMPHAEACEAE

Nymphaea is the principal genus of this small but distinctive family, popularly called water lilies. It is cosmopolitan and represented in South Africa by four species of which the most widespread is the mauve-blue Cape water lily, *N. capensis.*

This species formerly occurred in vleis on the Cape Peninsula but is now extinct there, although it still survives in dams, vleis and in quiet backwaters of major rivers in many other parts of the country.

Two other indigenous water lilies which do not reach the Cape, are found in South Africa. *Nymphaea caerulea,* a blue-flowered Transvaal species, is commoner while *N. lotus,* with creamy white flowers, is seen only occasionally in Zululand and the warmer parts of the Transvaal.

146. *Nymphaea capensis:* Water lily, Paddapreekstoel

DROSERACEAE

147. *Drosera cistiflora:* Sundew, Doublom

150. *Drosera hilaris*

151. *Drosera trinervia*

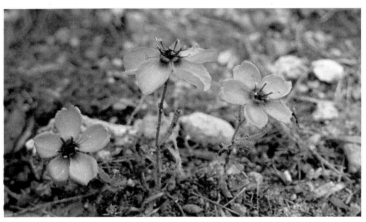

148. *Drosera cistiflora:* Sundew, Doublom

These captivating, insectivorous plants, called sundews, belong to the genus *Drosera* of which there are 18 species South Africa. They are easily recognised by their leaves whic are covered with sticky, sensitive, stalked glands. Flies and oth small insects are trapped in these glands and are absorbed augment the plants' nitrogen supply.

Drosera cistiflora, a large-flowered Western Cape species, usually pink, white or cream but a brilliant scarlet colour form found at a few sites near Darling, north of Cape Town. *cistiflora* and the diminutive *D. trinervia* are both tuberous, dyi down and becoming dormant in summer and then sprouting a growing again with the advent of winter rains, while *D. hilaris* an evergreen herbaceous species.

149. *Drosera cistiflora:* Sundew, Doublom

152. *Drosera cistiflora:* Sundew, Doublom

BRASSICACEAE
(CRUCIFERAE)

The cabbage family has several representatives in South Africa but *Heliophila*, a genus of some 70 species, is the most important. Most heliophilas are delicate winter-growing annuals flowering in August and September. The majority have vivid blue flowers and are popularly called blue flax although several white and yellow flowered species are known. From the Darling-Malmesbury area of the Western Cape to Northern Namaqualand one can be sure that any large patch of intensely blue flowers seen in the veld during springtime is one or other of the heliophilas in bloom. They tend mainly to open on warm sunny days — the name *Heliophila* means sun-lover.

153. *Heliophila coronopifolia*

154. *Heliophila africana*

OCHNACEAE

Ochna and *Brackenridgea* are the only South African genera of this largely South American-centred family of tropical and sub-tropical trees and shrubs.

Ochna's have become much-loved garden shrubs especially *O. serrulata* and *O. natalitia*. Spectacular as their golden trusses of flowers may be in springtime, it is their gaudy fruits which catch the eye and indeed have inspired their common name, Mickey Mouse tree. After flowering the calyx-lobes turn red, reflexing to reveal the at first green and then later shiny black seeds. At this stage the whole structure looks uncommonly like a Mickey Mouse face!

Ochna is found from the Eastern Cape to Natal and the Transvaal.

155. *Ochna serrulata:* Mickey Mouse tree, Carnival bush, Rooihout

156. *Ochna natalitia:* Rooihout

157. *Ochna pulchra:* Wild pear, Wildepruim

CRASSULACEAE

Like several other predominantly succulent plant families, the cosmopolitan Crassulaceae is centred in South Africa where it has undergone great diversification, and adapted to a variety of habitats. Practically all are succulents: indeed, the family name is derived from the Latin, *crassus*, meaning thick.

Crassula, the largest genus, is represented here by over 140 species. In the Karoo and Namaqualand crassulas are plump, dwarf succulents with tightly overlapping leaves as in *C. pyramidalis* and *C. columnaris*. Others, like the scarlet *C. coccinea*, grow in the mistbelt region of the higher Cape peaks, while *C. fascicularis* is a herbaceous, fynbos species and *C. vaginata* is frequent in grassland habitats in the Transvaal and Natal. *C. ovata* from the Eastern Cape bush grows into a small tree up to three metres in height.

Cotyledon, a related genus, contains several species highly toxic to stock but the fleshy leaves of the variable and widespread *Cotyledon orbiculata* have long been successfully used to soften and remove corns and warts.

158. *Crassula pyramidalis:* Rygbossie

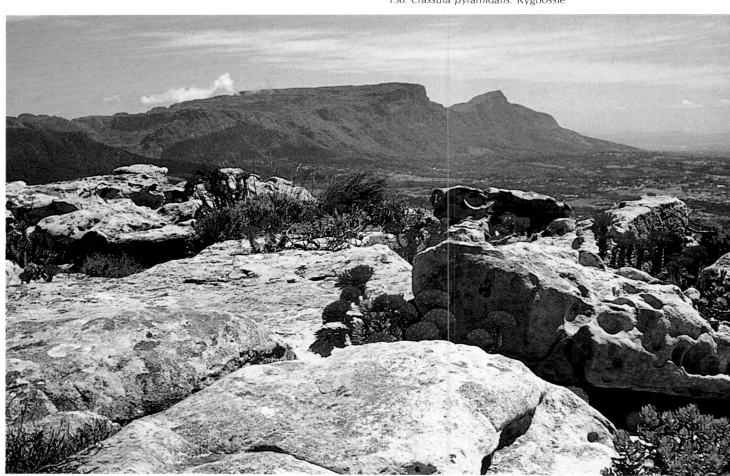

159. *Crassula coccinea:* Red crassula, Klipblom

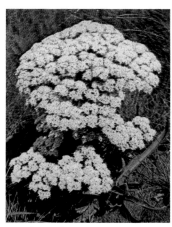

0. *Crassula fascicularis:* Klipblom   161. *Crassula coccinea:* Red crassula, Klipblom   162. *Crassula vaginata*

164. *Crassula fascicularis:* Klipblom

165. *Crassula corallina*

3. *Crassula columnaris*   166. *Crassula fascicularis:* Klipblom

59

167. *Cotyledon orbiculata:* Pig's ears, Varkore

168. *Crassula vaginata*

169. *Crassula ovata:* Karkay, Plakkies

170. *Crassula perfoliata:* Red crassula, Heuningbossie

CUNONIACEAE

1. *Cunonia capensis:* Red alder, Rooi-els

ROSACEAE

2. *Grielum humifusum:* Duikerwortel

Only two members of this small Southern Hemisphere family are found in South Africa — *Platylophus trifoliatus* and *Cunonia capensis,* better known as 'rooi-els'.

Cunonia capensis is a handsome forest tree, frequent in moist evergreen forests from the Cape to as far north as the Eastern Transvaal, often attaining 18 metres in height. Apart from producing beautiful timber, rooi-els is one of our most decorative trees. Creamy white flower spikes, like candles, appear among the dark glossy foliage in May and June, greatly enlivening the sombre forests at a time when few other trees are flowering.

C. capensis is an isolated outlier: all other species of *Cunonia* are confined to the Pacific island of New Caledonia.

The Rose family is a huge cosmopolitan assemblage of plants, many of them of great economic importance, but in South Africa represented by only about 120 species, mostly spiny, rather insignificant shrubs. *Grielum,* a genus of about five eye-catching species, is the only exception. These trailing annuals or perennials grow in winter, mainly in the more arid region of the Western Cape and Namaqualand. On warm, sunny springtime days their brilliant yellow, satin-textured flowers burst open, carpeting the veld with a dazzling but ephemeral display. Not surprisingly, many attempts have been made to cultivate these gorgeous plants away from their natural habitats, but hitherto without success. Even at Kirstenbosch where grielums have on occasion been grown, the flowers often fail to open properly due to insufficient light intensity.

BRUNIACEAE

This small but distinctive family of approximately eighty species occurs only in South Africa, and even here it is restricted to the Western and Southern Cape, growing almost exclusively on Table Mountain sandstone formations. They are heath-like shrubs with tiny flowers often massed in spherical heads. *Audouinia capitata*, a species confined to the Cape Peninsula, is heath-like in appearance while *Staavia* has

173. *Brunia stokoei:* Rooistompie

compound flowerheads resem bling those of the daisy famil *Brunia, Berzelia* and *Nebel* are the largest and mo typical genera with their mass ed, pom-pon-shaped flowe heads.

Berzelia lanuginosa, illu trated here, is one of the mo widespread species, an grows in dense stands partic larly along watercourses or seepage areas where its pr sence is a sure indicator perennial water.

174. *Staavia glutinosa:*
Flycatcher bush, Vlieëbossie

175. *Brunia nodiflora:*
Stompie, Fonteinbossie

176. *Berzelia lanuginosa:* Kol-kol

7. *Audouinia capitata:* False heath, Basterheide

178. *Berzelia lanuginosa:* Vleiknopbos, Kol-kol

). *Nebelia paleacea*

63

FABACEAE (LEGUMINOSAE)

180. *Aspalathus carnosa*

Leguminous plants (pod and bean bearers) constitute one of the largest and most economically important plant families in the world. Some botanists prefer to subdivide them into three separate families but it is more convenient to regard them as a single family, Fabaceae (or Leguminosae as it is alternatively called).

South Africa is well endowed with legumes to be found in every part of the country, many of them beautiful trees or shrubs. *Priestleya, Podalyria, Liparia* and *Hypocalyptus* are all from the fynbos area of the South Western Cape while *Adenolobus* is characteristic of the arid North Western Cape.

Soft-wooded herbaceous forms such as the widely dispersed *Sutherlandia frutescens* are also common. *Sutherlandia* is cultivated for both its flowers and its ornamental inflated pods, but is best known for its supposed medicinal properties. Com-

monly called 'kankerbossie' in country districts it is believed th an infusion of the leaves cures cancer.

Thorn trees, belonging to the genus *Acacia*, are also legum They are the most ubiquitous and typical of our native tre There are over 40 species indigenous to South Africa, fou throughout the country but especially in Natal and t Transvaal.

Their tiny yellow or cream flowers are massed in spheri clusters or slender cylindrical spikes. *Dichrostachys cinerea* common Transvaal tree, looks very like an *Acacia* but is eas distinguished by its bicoloured flower-spikes in pink and yello

In warmer parts of the Eastern Cape, Natal and Transvaal o is likely to encounter one or other of the more than eight nati species of *Erythrina*, or coral trees, surely the most spectacular

181. *Bauhinia galpinii:* Pride of De Kaap, Vlam-van-die-Vlakte

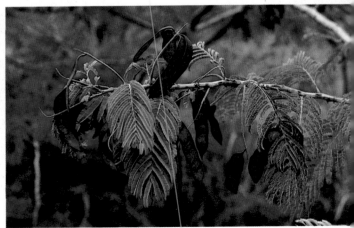

182. *Acacia ataxacantha:* Flame thorn, Vlamdoring

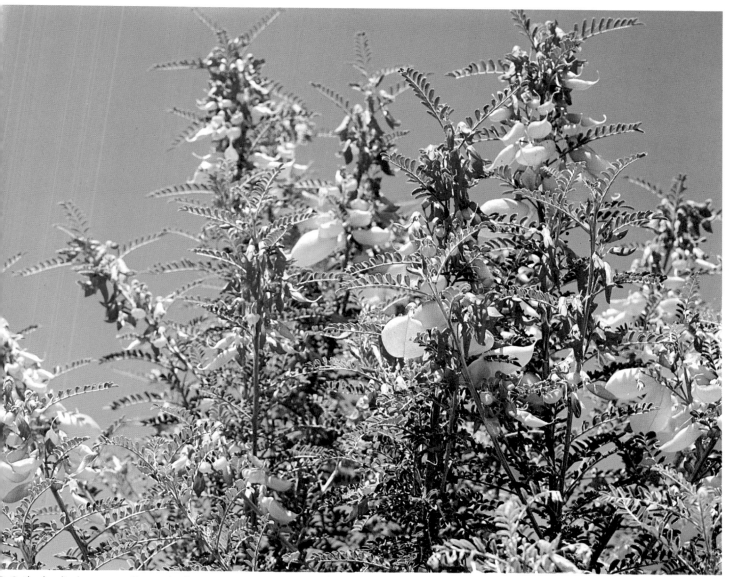

183. *Sutherlandia frutescens:* Cancer bush

. *Crotalaria doidgeae*

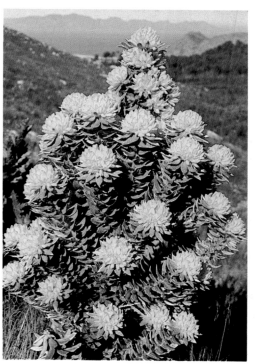

185. *Priestleya tomentosa:* Silver pea, Vaalertjie

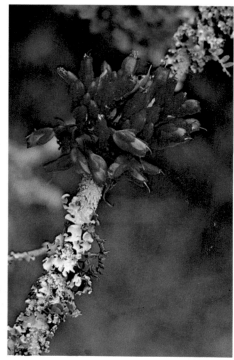

186. *Schotia afra:* Small-leaved Karoo
Boer-bean, Fynblaarkarooboerboon

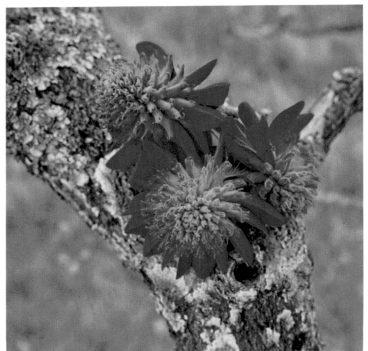

187. *Erythrina latissima*: Broad-leaved coral tree

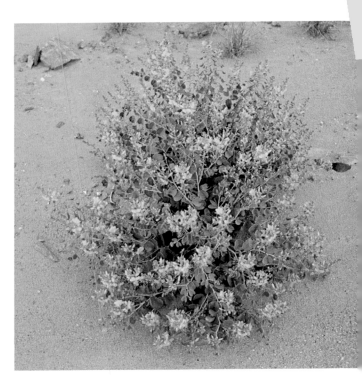

188. *Adenolobus pechuelii*

all our ornamental trees. Several species have the habit of producing trusses of scarlet blooms in late spring, just before the summer flush of new leaves has appeared.

Many legumes have nitrogen-fixing bacteria in nodules on their roots and so while we frequently tend to evaluate these plants in aesthetic terms it should be remembered that they play a key role in improving the nitrogen levels in the soil.

189. *Liparia splendens:*
Orange nodding-head,
Mountain dahlia, Geelkoppie

66

190. *Erythrina humeana:* Dwarf coral tree, Kleinkoraalboom

. *Dichrostachys cinerea:* Sickle bush, Sekelbos

192. *Bolusanthus speciosus:* Tree wistaria, Vanwykshout

Bolusanthus speciosus, although small in stature, is one of our most graceful trees. It is found in the Transvaal bushveld, producing pendulous sprays of mauve flowers in spring. They closely resemble *Wisteria* but are without any scent. The generic name *Bolusanthus* means 'Bolus flower' and honours Dr Harry Bolus, the pioneer Cape botanist who founded the Bolus Herbarium.

194. *Hypocalyptus sophoroides*

. *Acacia nebrownii:* Water thorn, Waterdoring

OXALIDACEAE

Most of the more than 200 South African species of *Oxalis* are found in Namaqualand and the South Western Cape, but a few such as *O. smithiana* reach Natal and the Eastern Transvaal. At the Cape they are the harbingers of winter, appearing almost everywhere and flowering from autumn throughout winter into spring. Their deep-seated bulbs are so sensitive to the change of season that even before the first autumn rains have fallen, early flowering species break through the parched earth and burst into bloom. They come in almost every colour except blue, either single flowers as in *O. purpurea* or massed together like a V torian posy as in *O. heidelbergensis*. Commonly called sorrel 'surings' because of the tart acidic flavour of the leaves ar stems, several species with fairly large, edible, nutty-flavoure bulbs are sometimes collected and eaten in the North Weste Cape: but this old practice is fast disappearing.

A few aquatic species are also known, such as *O. distic* which grows in temporary pools during winter. The leaves ar flowers float on the surface until the pool dries up in summ and appear again as it fills the following winter.

195. *Oxalis obtusa*

6. *Oxalis purpurea*

200. *Oxalis smithiana:* Rooisuring

7. *Oxalis tenella*

8. *Oxalis heidelbergensis*

201. *Oxalis polyphylla:* Vingersuring

9. *Oxalis luteola*

202. *Oxalis disticha*

69

203. *Monsonia speciosa:* Butterfly flower, Slangblom

204. *Erodium incarnatum*

GERANIACEAE

Almost half the known species which comprise the Geraniaceae are to be found in South Africa. Their characteristic fruits are an unmistakable family feature and have inspired several of the Greek-derived generic names such as *Geranium* (= crane's bill), *Pelargonium* (= stork's bill) and *Erodium* (= heron's bill). This allusion to birds' beaks is at once apparent if one examines the developing, pointed fruits. When ripe, the whole structure splits into five segments, explosively catapulting the seeds into the air for dispersal. *Geranium* itself is represented here by almost 18 species of which the best known is *G. incanum,* often seen along Southern Cape roads. *Geranium* and its other allies shown on this page are readily distinguished by having five petals of equal size whereas the *Pelargonium* does not.

Monsonia speciosa in pink, white or creamy-green tones is a handsome tuberous perennial which enlivens gravelly hills and flats in the Western Cape during spring. A sensitive deep-seated tuberous root system makes it a difficult and capricious species in cultivation.

Sarcocaulon is a shrubby genus mainly from the arid western regions of the Cape. They are commonly called Bushman's candles because their thick resinous stems are highly inflammable, blazing furiously if set alight.

205. *Sarcocaulon multifidum*

206. *Sarcocaulon herrei*

207. *Sarcocaulon patersonii:* Candlebush, Boesmanskers

70

8. *Monsonia speciosa:* Butterfly flower, Slangblom

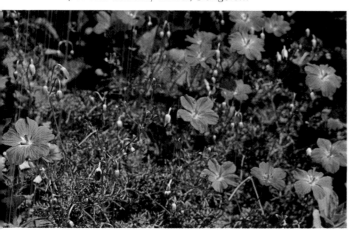

9. *Geranium incanum:* Vrouebossie, Bergtee

0. *Sarcocaulon crassicaule:* Candlebush, Boesmansdoring

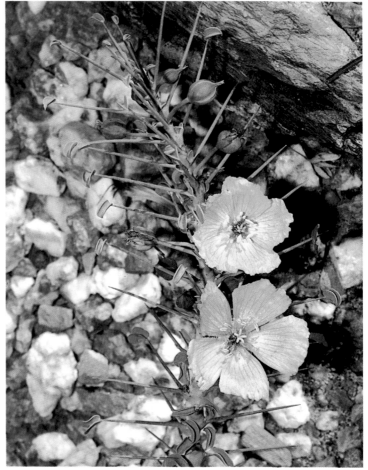

211. *Sarcocaulon l'heritieri*

PELARGONIUM

There is little doubt that the genus *Pelargonium* is South Africa's greatest contribution to the world's gardens. With more than 250 species indigenous here, this genus is the largest and most important in the Geraniaceae. Incidentally, the so-called 'geraniums' are in fact hybrids between various species of *Pelargonium*.

The scarlet-flowered *P. inquinans* and the pink *P. salmoneum* and *P. zonale* — all from the Eastern Cape bush — have contributed to the parentage of modern garden or zonal 'geraniums'.

Similarly, *P. lateripes* and *P. peltatum* from the Southern and Eastern Cape are the ancestors of the so-called 'ivy-leaved geraniums'.

These are some of the herbaceous or shrubby species, but in Namaqualand and in the Karoo many bizarre growth forms have been evolved. Some are tuberous with large turnip-like rootstocks, growing in winter and dying down in summer. Others have developed swollen succulent stems or are covered with spines. In high mountainous areas species such as *P. tricolor* from the Swartberg and also the Langeberg at Riversdale have a dwarf, tufted, almost alpine mode of growth. Indeed, in *Pelargonium* we see how a group of plants has diversified, evolved and adapted to the many ecological niches available to it.

212. *Pelargonium tricolor*

213. *Pelargonium inquinans:* Scarlet pelargonium, Wilde malva

215. *Pelargonium triste:* Kaneelblom

214. *Pelargonium oreophilum*

216. *Pelargonium hermanniaefolium*

. *Pelargonium lateripes*   218. *Pelargonium betulinum:* Birch-leaf pelargonium, Kanferblaar, Maagpynbossie, Suurbos

9. *Pelargonium cucullatum:* Hooded-leaf pelargonium, Tree pelargonium, Wilde malva

0. *Pelargonium magenteum*   221. *Pelargonium karooicum*

73

EUPHORBIACEAE

Euphorbias are found throughout the world in an amazing range of life forms from tropical trees to tiny annual herbs, but in South Africa they are nearly all succulents. *E. meloformis* is an extreme form from the Eastern Cape, reduced to a globe-like body, while others such as *E. cooperi* from the Transvaal and Zululand are large and tree-like. All euphorbias have latex canals in their tissues so that when leaves or stems are cut a milky juice at once flows from the wound. Usually this latex is severely irritant but certain species like *E. virosa* from near the Orange River mouth produce highly toxic latex, so toxic that it was used by the Bushmen as an ingredient in their arrow-poisons.

Most of our euphorbias are stem-succulents, that is, their stems are green and swollen, filled with water-storing tissues, b their leaves are either vestigial or soon drop off. Only in a fe species such as *E. hamata* from the Clanwilliam district do som leaves persist for any length of time. In this species they ofte become suffused with red pigments.

Sometimes succulent euphorbias' stems are tightly compre sed and so the adult plant grows to form a hard mound as is see in *E. pulvinata* from the North Eastern Cape.

A similar but looser growth habit is seen in *E. caput-medusa* from the Cape West Coast, so named because its lax, contorte stems resemble the writhing snakes on the head of the Gorgc Medusa.

222. *Euphorbia meloformis*: Eselskos, Bobbejaankos, Skilpadkos

223. *Euphorbia caput-medusae*: Medusa's head, Vingerpol

224. *Euphorbia virosa*: Boesmansgif

225. *Euphorbia esculenta*: Soetvingerpol

226. *Euphorbia ledienii*: Noorsdoring, Suurnoors

227. *Euphorbia hamata*: Olifantsmelkbos

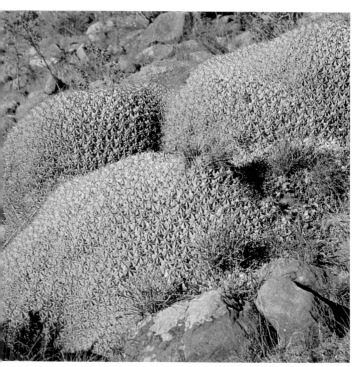

8. *Euphorbia pulvinata:* Pincushion, Voetangel

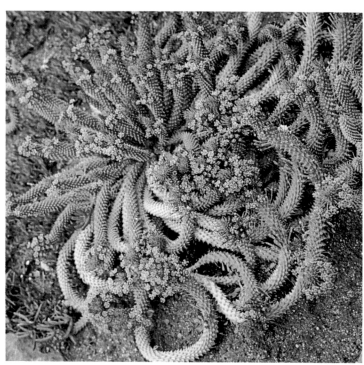

229. *Euphorbia caput-medusae:* Medusa's head, Vingerpol

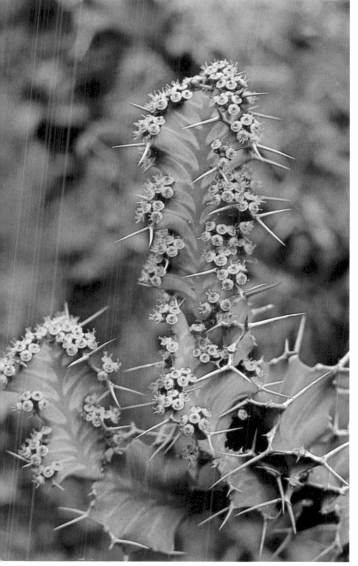

0. *Euphorbia grandicornis:* Transvaal candelabra tree

231. *Euphorbia cooperi:* Transvaalse kandelaarnaboom

RUTACEAE

It is not easy to associate the familiar tropical Asian members of this family belonging to the genus *Citrus* with their largely heath-like South African relatives: yet a common factor — the presence of numerous volatile-oil-producing glands on their vegetative parts — is an easily recognisable unifying feature. However, *Calodendrum capense*, a beautiful tree of our evergreen forests producing chestnut-like fruits, does bear some resemblance to its tropical relatives.

Nevertheless, the Rutaceae in South Africa are concentrated mainly in the Western Cape where *Agathosma* and *Adenandra* are important genera. All are heathy, strongly aromatic shrubs to which a generalised name buchu is often applied. Real buchu, *Agathosma crenulata* and oval-leaved buchu, *Agathosma betulina*, were used as blood purifiers even before the advent of Western man at the Cape, and are still extensively prescribed in herbal remedies for kidney complaints. *Adenandra villosa* is one of the larger flowered, more ornamental species from among the Cape Rutaceae which in general are known more for their foliar fragrance than floral splendour.

76

232. *Calodendrum capense*: Cape chestnut, Wildekastaiing

233. *Adenandra villosa*: China flower, Betsie

POLYGALACEAE

he Polygalaceae or milkwort family frequently gives rise to
me confusion among non-botanists because the flower has a
perficial resemblance to those of the pea-flowered legumes.
olygala itself is cosmopolitan, comprising some 600 species,
th about 100 in South Africa. *P. virgata* and *P. myrtifolia*, both
*o*m the Cape, are attractive shrubs occasionally seen in cultiva-
*o*n, but few of our other species are especially noteworthy.
*o*st polygalas have purple flowers but in *Nylandtia*, a related
*o*nus endemic to the Cape, white forms occasionally appear.
vlandtia is also unusual in that after flowering, instead of dry
*o*eds, it produces a crop of juicy edible berries. These bright
*o*ange berries are called 'skilpadbessies' and are much loved by
*o*ildren and birds alike.

The name *Polygala* means 'much milk', alluding to an ancient
*o*t unsubstantiated belief that cows increase their milk yields if
*o*lowed to browse on these plants. However, the powdered roots
o several local species are prescribed as a purgative and ver-
*o*fuge by Zulu herbalists.

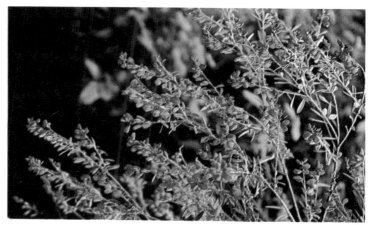

236. *Nylandtia spinosa:* Duinbessie, Skilpadbessie

237. *Polygala virgata:* Bloukappie

4. *Nylandtia spinosa:* Duinbessie, Skilpadbessie

5. *Polygala myrtifolia:* Septemberbossie, Blouertjieboom

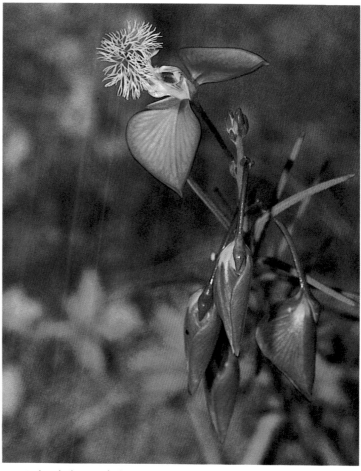

238. *Polygala bracteolaris*

ICACINACEAE

Although popularly called white pear, *Apodytes dimidiata* is in no way related to the familiar table fruit of that name but was probably so called because its pale timber closely resembles pear wood. In the 19th century Cape waggon builders prized this timber for its tough elastic qualities. Although found in almost all temperate evergreen forests from the Cape Peninsula to Ethiopia, *Apodytes dimidiata* is not particularly distinctive except when in fruit. That stage is shown here with a cluster of ripe black seeds and their bright orange supporting arils.

AITONIACEAE

Chinese lantern tree and 'klapperbossie' are both appropriate and familiar names for this very decorative little tree which enlivens the Little Karoo's landscape in winter and spring. As spring and early summer advance, its comparatively dull pink flowers fade, giving way to plump crimson fused pods. Many gardeners have unsuccessfully attempted to grow *Nymania capensis*: it will only flourish in arid or semi-arid areas. A small-leaved form is found in the North Western Cape.

239. *Apodytes dimidiata:* White pear, Witpeer

240. *Nymania capensis:* Chinese lanterns, Klapperbos

SAPINDACEAE

his family is closely related to the Aitoniaceae and indeed the
amaqualand red balloon, *Erythrophysa alata*, a small shrub
om rocky koppies in the North Western Cape, is often mistaken
r *Nymania*. *Erythrophysa* is easily recognised by its compound
aves; *Nymania* has simple leaves.

BOMBACACEAE

e baobab, *Adansonia digitata*, is probably Africa's most
mous tree. In our country it grows only in warm, dry parts of
e North Eastern Transvaal, ranging as far south as the Sout-
nsberg and Olifants River.

Its huge, white, sweetly scented flowers, believed to be
llinated by bats, precede large egg-shaped pods. When broken
en these pods reveal numerous seeds embedded in a spongy
ite pulp with a faint flavour reminiscent of sherbert — hence
e baobab's other popular name, cream-of-tartar tree.

Animals often chew baobab stems to relieve their thirst in
nes of drought because, despite its massive bulky trunk, the
sues of *Adansonia* are soft, pulpy and rather watery.

TILIACEAE

armannia africana, commonly called the Cape stock rose,
longs to the jute family, a group of plants noted for the com-
ercial importance of their fibres. Many years ago attempts
re made to exploit *Sparmannia* fibres commercially in the
orms River area but their quality failed to match that of Asian
e and the project was abandoned. Nevertheless, it is a most
corative soft-wooded tree — an old favourite as a tub plant in
ctorian conservatories. It is frequent along streamside and
rest margins between George and Humansdorp in the Southern
pe, flowering in early winter.

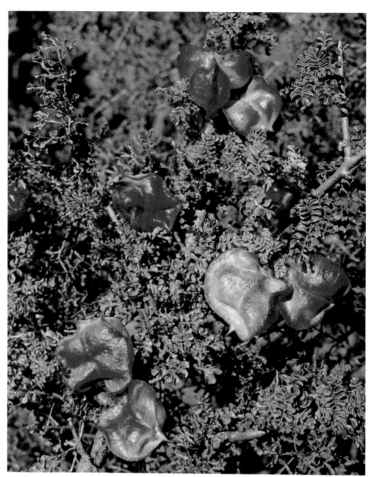

241. *Erythrophysa alata*: Namaqualand red balloon

. *Sparmannia africana*: Cape stock rose, Kaapse stokroos

243. *Adansonia digitata*: Baobab, Kremetartboom

RHAMNACEAE

There are some 150 species of *Phylica* in South Africa, mainly concentrated in the South Western Cape where they are important constituents of fynbos vegetation. Their flowers are so tiny that they must be viewed through a hand-lens. But they are amply compensated for such diminutive flowers by the presence of numerous feathery to silky sub-tending bracts in white, pink, grey or golden shades which in certain species render each flowerhead quite spectacularly conspicuous. Phylicas are mainly shrubs or small trees, especially prominent in dry, mountainous country like the Cedarberg and Cold Bokkeveld.

244. *Phylica marlothii*

245. *Phylica dodii*

246. *Phylica stipularis:* Hondegesiggie

247. *Phylica pubescens:* Featherhead, Veerkoppie

248. *Phylica rigida*

Greyia sutherlandii: Natal bottlebrush

GREYIACEAE

There are only three species of *Greyia*, all from South Africa. Some botanists assign them to the family Melianthaceae but many classify them in a distinct, exclusively South African family, Greyiaceae. These soft-wooded shrubs or small trees from the Eastern Cape, Natal and the Transvaal are rather similar in appearance, producing, in late winter and early spring, masses of dense, scarlet flower-spikes at the tips of their bare branches. *Greyia sutherlandii* — Natal bottlebrush — is the best-known species, for it is such a conspicuous feature of crags or forest margins in the Natal Drakensberg and is also finding its way into more and more private gardens as a decorative ornamental.

). *Greyia sutherlandii:* Natal bottlebrush

MALVACEAE

Hibiscus, the largest genus of the mallow family, comprises some 300 species of which at least 30 are found in South Africa. Some are diminutive herbs like *H. trionum* while others like *H. tiliaceus*, a coastal species from Natal, grow into six-metre-tall trees. *H. tiliaceus*, often found associated with mangrove swamps, is the source of a useful fibre for making ropes, sails and fishing nets in sub-tropical and tropical areas bordering the Indian Ocean.

A distinctive feature of this family is that the stamens are united to form a tubular column in the centre of each flower.

251. *Hibiscus vitifolius:* Hibiscus, Wildestokroos

252. *Hibiscus aethiopicus*

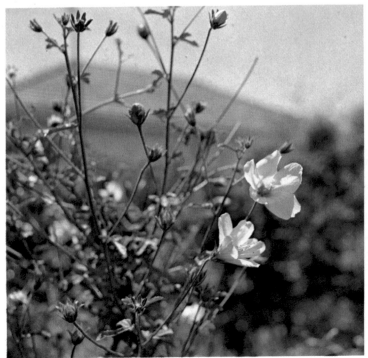

253. *Hibiscus pedunculatus:* Hibiscus, Wildestokroos

254. *Hibiscus pusillus*

5. *Hibiscus tiliaceus:* Wild cotton tree, Wilde katoenboom

5. *Pavonia columella*

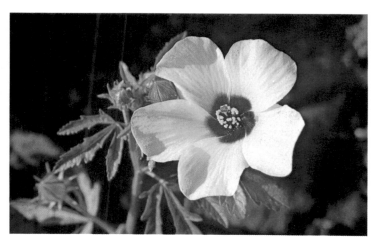

257. *Hibiscus trionum:* Black-eyed Susan, Terblanzbossie

83

STERCULIACEAE

This largely tropical to sub-tropical family of woody plants has many decorative representatives in our country. Of the several species of *Dombeya* that are found in Natal and the Transvaal, *D. burgessiae*, a pretty pink-and-white flowered shrub from the Lowveld, is now grown in many gardens: while the so-called wild pear, *D. rotundifolia* from the Transvaal bushveld, is without doubt one of our most spectacular trees. In late winter and spring its bare branches are covered with pure white blooms — an unforgettable display when seen against a dusty brown bushveld landscape.

Trees of the genus *Sterculia* — popularly called Lowve chestnuts — are known not so much for their flowers as for the decorative seed pods. After these hard, woody pods have sp open and released their seeds, they are often collected for use dried flower arrangements or used as novel ashtrays.

But *Hermannia,* with some 200 species in South Africa, is by f the most important genus of this family in our region. Herma nias are found in arid and semi-arid environments, and a especially common in the Karoo where they are promine among the Little Karoo bushes which, in that desolate area, miraculously sustain great flocks of sheep. Most hermanni have insignificant yellow flowers, but a few such as *H. stricta* a a lovely sight when in full bloom.

258. *Dombeya rotundifolia:* Common wild pear, Gewone drolpeer

84

9. *Dombeya burgessiae:* Pink wild pear (white form), Persdrolpeer 260. *Hermannia stricta:* Rooi-opslag

261. *Sterculia rogersii:* Common star chestnut, Gewone sterkastaiing

85

2. *Sterculia rogersii:* Common star chestnut, Gewone sterkastaiing 263. *Sterculia murex:* Lowveld chestnut, Laeveld kastaiing

PENAEACEAE

The Penaeaceae is one of several plant families to be found only in South Africa. This small but very distinct family consists of 25 species, all endemic to the South Western Cape. They are found mainly in mountainous country, growing almost exclusively on poor sandy soils derived from Table Mountain sandstone.

Most species are characterised by their very restricted distribution ranges. *Brachysiphon imbricatus* for example grows only on the Cape Peninsula while *Endonema retzioides* has an even more limited range in the Riviersonderend Mountains. But by far the most restricted of all is *Glischrocolla formosa,* an exceptiona[l] rare shrublet known from only a few stands in the French Ho[ek] and Hottentots Holland Mountains. One of the rarest Ca[pe] plants, it was discovered in 1790 by Francis Masson, plant colle[c]tor to the Royal Botanic Gardens at Kew, who gather[ed] specimens in the French Hoek Mountains: but no furth[er] specimens were seen until 1932 when Thomas Stokoe found [a] small colony in the Hottentots Holland Mountains abo[ve] Somerset West.

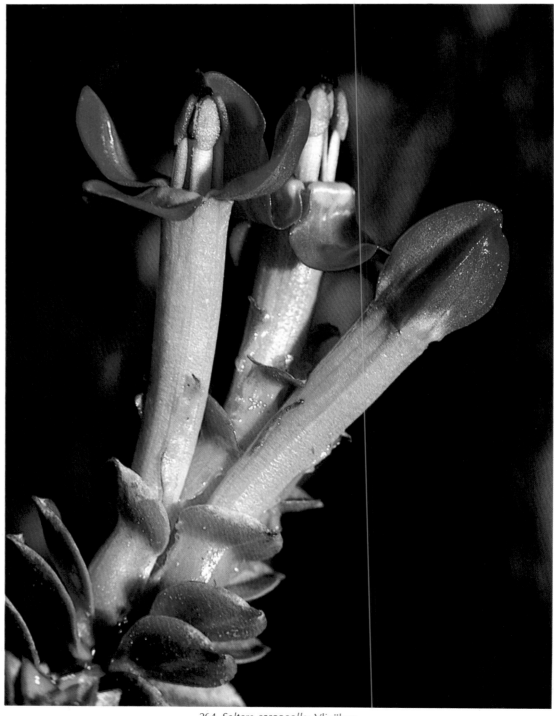

264. *Saltera sarcocolla:* Vlieëbos

Fortunately, *Saltera sarcocolla,* the most attractive member of ̣e family, is fairly widespread from the Cape Peninsula to ̣edasdorp. It shows the family's characteristic floral structure ̣a colourful four-lobed calyx tube with no petals. *Saltera* is very ̣riable in form and colour, with both pink and white, long and ̣ort tubed variations found within a single species.

̣Most Penaeaceae are small heath-like shrubs growing in open ̣ld, but a few such as *Sonderothamnus petraeus* are rock ̣vellers, surviving quite happily rooted in bare rock crevices.

265. *Saltera sarcocolla:* Vlieëbos

266. *Sonderothamnus petraeus*

̣7. *Glischrocolla formosa*

̣8. *Endonema retzioides*

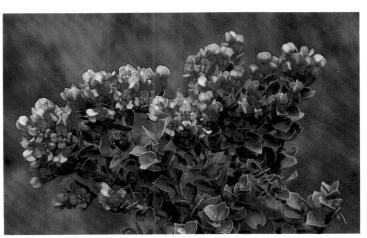

269. *Brachysiphon imbricatus:* Sissies

THYMELAEACEAE

The Thymelaeaceae or Daphne family is cosmopolitan in its range, but especially abundant in South Africa where the majority of species are centred in the South Western Cape. *Gnidia* (70 species) and *Struthiola* (40 species) are the largest genera. An important family character is that the calyx is a brightly-coloured tube, while the petals are usually reduced to dull inconspicuous scales at the mouth of the calyx tube. Another unmistakable character is the exceedingly tough bark which splits longitudinally into fibrous strips like rope strands. Most South African Thymelaeaceae are common components of the Cape fynbos where they are generally small heath-like shrubs, but a few, such as *Gnidia kraussiana* found over much of the interior of South Africa, are more widespread. This latter species is commonly called 'gifbossie', for it is exceedingly poisonous to domestic stock — a mere handful of leaves is enough to kill a horse or cow.

Lachnaea, the 'bergasters', are handsome shrubs from high altitudes in the Cape mountains but few have ever been successfully cultivated. Fortunately the pompon tree, *Dais cotinifolia*, has adapted well to cultivation and is now grown throughout South Africa and in many other warm parts of the world. It is one of the few trees in this family and is found in the eastern parts of the country between East London and the Northern Transvaal.

270. *Lachnaea filamentosa*: Bergaster

271. *Dais cotinifolia*: Pompon tree

272. *Lachnaea buxifolia*

273. *Gnidia kraussiana*: Gifbossie

274. *Struthiola dodecandra*:
Katstertjie, Soetgonna

5. *Gnidia penicillata*

276. *Gnidia tomentosa*

7. *Gnidia polycephala*: Besembos, Januariebos

FLACOURTIACEAE

There are only a few representatives of this essentially tropical family in our region. All are woody shrubs, mostly with insignificant flowers. However, *Xylotheca kraussiana* — aptly named the African dogrose (although it is in no way related to true roses) — is an exception. This evergreen shrub or small tree grows in coastal forests in Natal and Zululand. Its fragrant flowers are followed by large woody seed capsules, filled with striking black and red seeds.

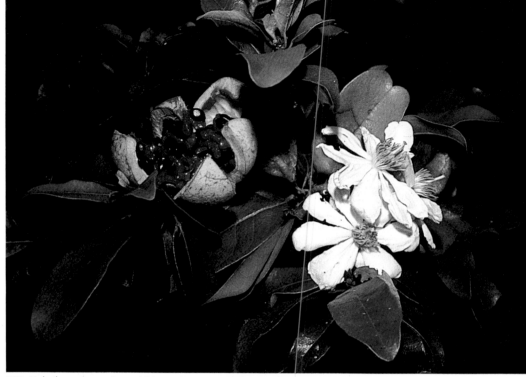

278. *Xylotheca kraussiana:* African dogrose, Afrikaanse hondsroos

PASSIFLORACEAE

To this family belongs the granadilla or passion fruit, a delicious South American representative of the family, so familiar on fruit stalls and in gardens.

However, the African Passifloraceae, unlike their transatlantic cousins, have a sinister reputation: despite its alluring fruits, *Adenia digitata* is virulently poisonous. Several human fatalities have been reported from the Transvaal, Natal and Botswana, where this tuberous-rooted vine occurs naturally. Death usually follows a few hours after eating the tempting fruits. There are some nine other species of *Adenia* in South Africa and all should be avoided. They have massive turnip-like rootstocks from which trailing stems emerge with the onset of the summer rains. Small, dull-coloured tubular flowers are produced in early summer followed by the colourful fruits, shown here.

Adenias are today much sought after by collectors of succulents who prize the grotesque forms of their bloated rootstocks.

279. *Adenia digitata:* Bobbejaangif

CUCURBITACEAE

en non-botanists can hardly fail to recognise members of the
curbitaceae — the pumpkin, cucumber and marrow family.
curbits are difficult to classify because their flowers are so
hilar but their fruits show great diversity and more often than
t are the most reliable means of identification. They are mostly
nual trailing vines, germinating with the onset of summer rains,
wering, and then producing their fruits in autumn.

Acanthosicyos naudiniana, a type of wild cucumber or 'tsamma', is common in the North Western Cape. It is an important
water source for the Bushmen who also roast the pips and then
grind them up to form an edible meal.

Cucumis africanus is found in many other dry parts of South
Africa as well as in the North Eastern Cape. This species is also
edible but should be treated with caution as bitter-tasting
mutants occasionally appear containing a poisonous principle.

In warmer sub-tropical areas like Natal, the genus *Momordica*
predominates. Momordicas are usually climbers, scrambling
amongst shrubs or over bushes with their beautiful fruits draped
among the branches. The Zulu use an infusion of *Momordica in-
volucrata* as a sedative for an upset stomach.

). *Acanthosicyos naudiniana:* Tsamma, Wildekomkommer

. *Cucumis africanus:* Wild cucumber

282. *Cucumis metuliferus:* Rooi-agurkie, Wildekomkommer

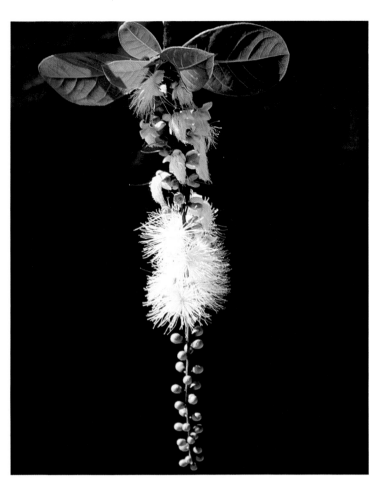

LECYTHIDACEAE

Barringtonia racemosa is the only member of the Lecythidace[ae] in South Africa, where it is popularly called the powder-puff tr[ee]. Like the other 38 Indo-Pacific species of *Barringtonia, B. r[ac-] emosa* is a mangrove. It grows in most warm, humid are[as] bordering the Indian and Pacific Oceans, extending down t[he] East African coast to Natal. Mangrove is a term used to descri[be] trees of various families which have adapted to life on coas[tal] mudflats, estuaries or inlets in the tropics. They are subjected [to] salty inundations with every high tide but have evolved vari[ous] methods of surviving this exposure, such as breathing ro[ots] which stand clear of the high water mark.

In *B. racemosa*, large oval seeds follow the delicate powd[er-] puff-like flowers. Each seed is enclosed in a light spongy cas[ing] giving it a high degree of buoyancy. When mature they fall to t[he] mud below and then float away on the next high tide. Germi[na-] tion follows almost immediately. Soon the floating seed anch[ors] itself and at once begins to grow into a new tree.

283. *Barringtonia racemosa:* Powder-puff tree, Poeierkwasboom

284. A mangrove setting with *Avicennia marina* (Verbenaceae) and seedlings of *Bruguiera gymnorrhiza* (Rhizophoraceae)

MELASTOMACEAE

veral exotic South American species of *Tibouchina* and *Lasian-*
a are commonly grown in our gardens, so this pan-tropical
mily is generally fairly familiar here. But only a few members
the Melastomaceae are indigenous to South Africa where they
e found in the warmer, moister parts of the Eastern Transvaal
along the Natal coast. The curiously jointed stamens are a
tinctive feature of the family.

Dissotis, an African genus of some 140 species, is represented
South Africa by only two species, *D. princeps,* a large-flowered
rub which is particularly common in swampy ground along the
tal coast, and by the smaller-flowered *D. canescens* from the
stern Transvaal escarpment.

Purple, pink and pure white colour forms of *D. princeps* are
own. It is especially suited to cultivation in wet boggy soil and
ows surprisingly well at Kirstenbosch where it makes a fine
play in February.

Dissotis canescens has smaller flowers of a clear rosy pink.

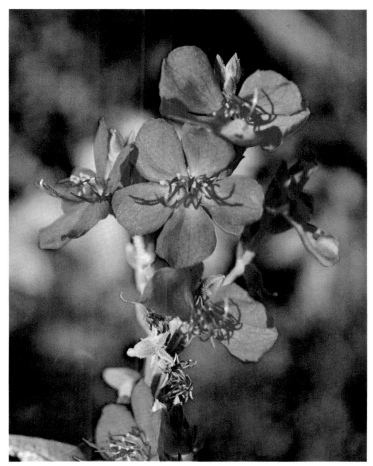

285. *Dissotis canescens:* Ordeal bean

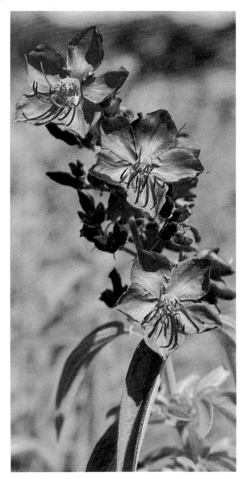

. *Dissotis princeps:* Kalwerbossie

287. *Dissotis princeps:* Kalwerbossie

288. *Dissotis princeps:* Kalwerbossie

COMBRETACEAE

Combretums are found in almost all the warmer parts of the world, except Australia. In Africa they are especially abundant and are very conspicuous in the savannahs. *Terminalia* (nine species) and *Combretum* (20 species) are our largest genera. Nearly all are trees or shrubs with rather dull insignificant flowers but very decorative four-winged, angular seed pods. *Combretum paniculatum* var. *microphyllum* is exceptional in that it is a rampant scrambler, covered with great sprays of scarlet flowers in summer. This lovely creeper is found in hot valleys in the Transvaal Lowveld. Its gorgeous blooms are followed in autumn by clusters of pinkish, angular fruits, equally attractive in their own right.

289. *Combretum paniculatum* var. *microphyllum*

94

290. *Combretum paniculatum* var. *microphyllum:* Flame creeper, Vlamklimop

ERICACEAE

a is the largest genus of flowering plants in South Africa. Well r 620 species are found in this country while there are prob- y many more as yet undescribed. Heaths do occur in other ts of the world such as the East African highlands, around the diterranean basin and in Western Europe — amounting to 1e 28 species — but the occurrence of over 600 species all

massed in the South Western Cape remains a botanical mystery. On the Cape Peninsula alone there are 103 species of *Erica*.

No other group of plants is more important a component of fynbos vegetation than the heaths. There is scarcely a habitat to which they have not been able to adapt. Ericas grow on coastal headlands, open flats, in bare rock crevices, along streamsides, in

. *Erica blenna:* Lantern heath

292. *Erica corydalis:* White petticoat heath

293. *Erica decora:* Sticky rose heath

. *Erica densifolia:* Sticky red-and-green heath, Knysnaheide

295. *Erica fastigiata* and *Moraea fugax*

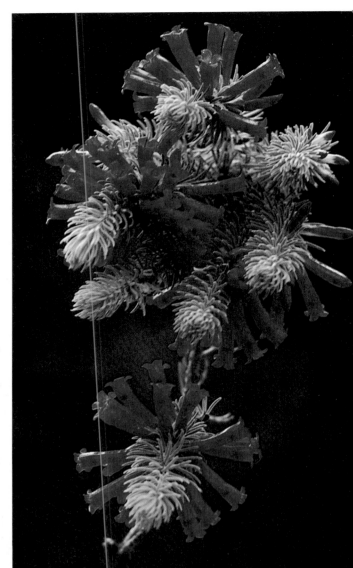

296. *Erica mammosa:* Nine-pin heath, Rooiklossieheide

297. *Erica longiflora*

96

298. *Erica junonia*

Erica decora and Leucadendron laureolum

boggy swamps and on the summits of our highest peaks. They flower throughout the year, with a different species coming into bloom almost every week. Indeed, one can take a walk in the Cape mountains any day of the year and find several different heaths in full bloom. Few other plant groups can match such seasonal and floral diversity.

Ericas take many different shapes and colours. The large, long-tubed species are among the most striking, like *E. mammosa* and *E. dichrus*. Both are robust species which have become popular garden sub-

Erica dichrus

301. *Erica viscaria:* Sticky heath, Klokkiesheide

jects. Not all heaths take easily to cultivation, especially th[e] from the summits of high mountains such as the graceful, lo[ng] necked *E. junonia*. This rarity from the Cold Bokkeveld Mo[un] tains has proved difficult to grow away from its natural habi[tat].

This page gives some idea of the great floral diversity of C[ape] heaths. It is hardly surprising that early botanical explorers w[ere] entranced by these charming little shrubs and soon introduc[ed] them to great private collections. During the late eighteenth a[nd] early nineteenth centuries the cult of growing Cape heaths [in] Europe reached its climax. The then Duke of Bedford had seve[ral] hundred species in cultivation by 1800. In recent years there [has] been a revival of interest in ericas, and many South Africans n[ow] grow them in their own gardens.

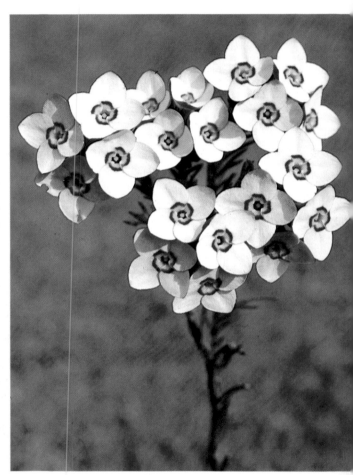

303. *Erica fastigiata:* Four sisters heath

302. *Erica curviflora:* Waterbos

304. *Erica melanthera*

. *Erica onosmaeflora*

. *Erica bruniades:* Kapokkie

308. *Erica tegulaefolia:* Banketheide

. *Erica massonii:* Houw Hoek heath, Taaiheide

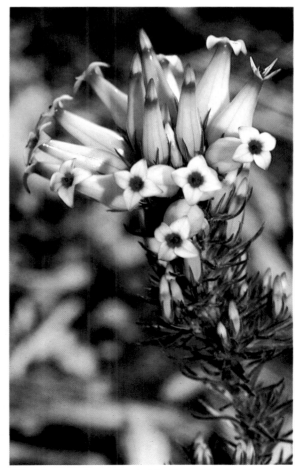

309. *Erica ventricosa:* Washeide, Franschhoekheide

99

GENTIANACEAE

In Europe members of this cosmopolitan family usually have vivid blue flowers such as the famous blue gentians of the Alps, but in South Africa they are only pink, yellow or white.

These rather delicate annual or perennial herbs are found mainly in the moister parts of the country. *Chironia* (15 species) and *Sebaea* (41 species) are the largest South African genera.

A few species do grow at high elevations, and indeed *Sebaea thodeana* from the Drakensberg and Lesotho is somewhat reminiscent of certain European gentians except for its colour.

Some have adapted to more arid situations such as *Orphium frutescens,* a woody shrublet which grows in brackish soils in coastal areas and has exquisite pink flowers that appear to be sculpted from wax.

311. *Orphium frutescens:* Teeringbos

310. *Sebaea exacoides:* Naeltjiesblom

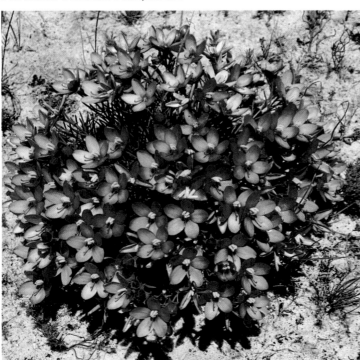

312. *Chironia linoides ssp. emarginata*

313. *Sebaea thodeana*

. Plumbago auriculata: Plumbago, Syselbos

. Plumbago auriculata: Plumbago, Syselbos

PLUMBAGINACEAE

Blue *Plumbago auriculata* is said to have been the favourite flower of Cecil Rhodes. It is a native of the Eastern Cape, Natal and Eastern Transvaal, where it grows as a straggling shrub or scrambler. But in cultivation, with clipping and shaping, it can soon be coaxed to form one of the most beautiful formal hedges one could wish for. It is almost always pale blue but rare white-flowered mutants are occasionally encountered.

Limonium perigrinum, the largest of our sea lavenders, is common in coastal bush along the Cape West Coast near Saldanha Bay. These are among the hardiest members of the family, well able to survive prolonged droughts as well as brackish soil yet producing masses of papery pink blooms each year without fail.

316. *Limonium perigrinum:* Sea lavender, Strandroos, Papierblom

OLEACEAE

ost non-botanists do not associate olives and jasmine, yet they th belong to the same plant family. In South Africa there are ur indigenous olives (though none is large enough to eat), and a indigenous jasmines. *Jasminum multipartitum* is the most corative of our native species. It has large flowers and is en-wed with a delicious fragrance. This handsome evergreen ub is found on dry koppies or in scrub and bush throughout e Eastern Cape, Natal and parts of the Eastern Transvaal. It is ng grown in more and more gardens, often displacing the miliar domesticated Asiatic jasmines.

317. *Jasminum multipartitum:* Wild jasmine

APOCYNACEAE

Most members of this family are found in the tropics where they are usually evergreen trees, shrubs or climbers, but in South Africa, especially in warmer drier areas, they are often stem succulents. A good example is the impala lily, *Adenium obesum*, familiar to all visitors to the Kruger Park. Its magnificent blooms are produced during winter and early spring in clusters at the tips of fleshy, swollen stems.

In North Western Namaqualand *Pachypodium namaquanum* adopts a similar mode of growth in response to arid environmental conditions. Cylindrical trunks — only rarely branched — are topped by clusters of leaves during the brief winter growing period. Namaqualanders call this weird tree 'halfmens' because, when seen in silhouette against an evening skyline, it seems like a ghostly human apparition. Avaricious succulent collectors have long prized the bizarre 'halfmens' which today is officially classed as an endangered species. Large specimens reach great ages: the one seen here is probably well over one hundred years old.

Whether succulent or shrubby, most Apocynaceae have milky white sap, and many are characterised by the presence of poisonous alkaloids in the tissue. Consequently, members of this family are best treated as poisonous, but there are exceptions such as the genus *Carissa* which bears edible fruits.

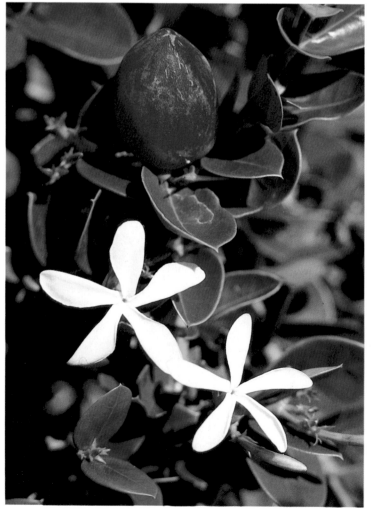

318. *Carissa macrocarpa*: Natal plum, Amatungulu, Grootnoem-noem

319. *Pachypodium namaquanum*: Elephant's trunk, Halfmens

Adenium obesum: Impala lily, Impalalelie

321. *Stapelia flavopurpurea*

322. *Duvalia reclinata:* Hottentotstoontjie, Kabietjie

ASCLEPIADACEAE

Shrubby and herbaceous members of this great tropical to sub-tropical family are commonly called milkweeds because of an abundance of milky latex in their sap. *Pachycarpus*, a herbaceous grassland genus from Natal and the Transvaal, is a typical example.

In South Africa, however, the tribe Stapeliae is dominant. These are stem succulents with watery rather than milky sap, varying in size from metre-high genera like *Hoodia* to miniature forms such as *Duvalia* and *Huernia*. They have evolved some of the most exotic and architecturally bizarre flowers in the plant kingdom with some of the most complex floral structures and equally complex pollination mechanisms. Most stapeliad flowers give off strongly foetid odours on opening, recalling various forms of organic decay. Attracted by these odours bluebottles and other flies swarm over the open blooms and in so doing pick up pollen and transfer it to another flower. Pollen is formed in two tiny waxy sacs linked by a yoke-like arm, which hooks in a fly's foot and is then transported to another flower of the same species where it slots perfectly into a stigmatic groove. The 'fit' varies from species to species but is so precise as to be a 'lock and key' mechanism. If pollination is effected, two V-shaped pods are formed rather like the horns of a goat, and so many country folk call stapeliads 'bokhoringtjies'. An old Hottentot word 'ghaap' is also currently used but refers more specifically to edible species. In Namaqualand their fleshy angular stems are still eaten fresh, pickled or preserved in syrup.

323. *Huernia zebrina*

324. *Pachycarpus grandiflorus*

. *Hoodia gordonii:* Wildeghaap

. *Trichocaulon flavum:* Ghaap

327. *Huerniopsis decipiens:* Kalkoennetjie

328. *Caralluma armata:* Aroena

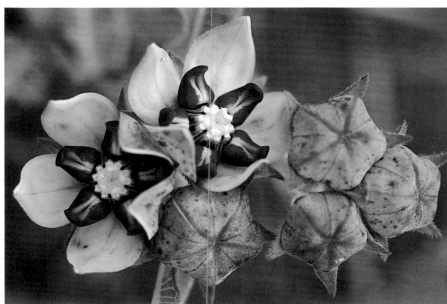

329. *Microloma tenuifolia:* Wax creeper, Kannetjie

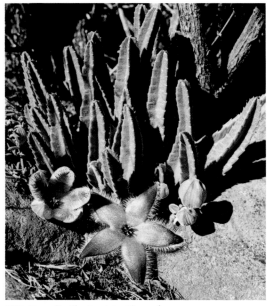

330. *Stapelia flavirostris:* Slangghaap

331. *Pachycarpus scaber*

332. *Caralluma villetii*

333. *Brachystelma barberae:* Platvoetaasblom

Other members of the family are tuberous-rooted like *Micro-* *ma*, the wax creeper which annually develops twining stems om an underground rootstock. *Brachystelma*, which grows iefly in summer rainfall areas, has enormous turnip-like tubers om which clusters of elegantly geometric flowers are produced spring and summer.

Orbeopsis lutea

CONVOLVULACEAE

Twiners, creepers and climbers predominate in this large family which is found in most parts of the world except the coldest regions. It is well developed in South Africa where about 120 species grow naturally.

Ipomoea, the largest genus, is cosmopolitan, with some 50 species in our area. Commonly called morning glories, their garishly coloured but delicate flowers open mainly in the cool of early morning. As the day wears on they wither, collapsing by evening, to be followed by another flower the next day. *Ipomoea crassipes* is a grassland species from the Eastern Cape and Natal. It is valued by certain African tribes for its alleged magical pro-

335. *Merremia kentrocaulos*

336. *Ipomoea pellita*

perties: the powdered root is used as a love charm or to prevent harm befalling a village. Ground-up roots are fed by the Zulu to their cattle if they wish to prevent anyone harming them.

While South African ipomoeas are predominantly pink or mauve-flowered, *Merremia* is a genus of white, cream or yellow-flowered climbers. *Merremia kentrocaulos* has a wide range in central and southern Africa. It is frequently seen in parts of the Transvaal during summer, either forming prostrate mats at the roadside or climbing to a height of 10 metres if suitable trees are available. Bushveld areas, especially the Kruger Park, are favoured habitats.

337. *Ipomoea crassipes*

BORAGINACEAE

The borage or forget-me-not family is a large, distinctive group of plants, mainly herbs and shrubs, found throughout the world but especially in Mediterranean regions. Their flowers are predominantly blue and their vegetative parts are invariably covered with characteristic stiff hairs or bristles. In South Africa *Lobostemon*, the largest genus, consisting of some 30 species, is centred in the South Western Cape and Namaqualand. Lobostemons are tough, drought-resistant shrubs found principally in semi-arid regions.

Lobostemon fruticosus is the most common and colourful species. It is locally abundant on dry hillsides in the South Western Cape, becoming very conspicuous for a few brief weeks

Lobostemon glaucophyllus

Lobostemon fruticosus: Luibossie, Agtdaegeneesbos

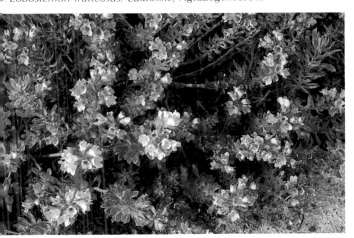

Lobostemon montanus

in spring when it is covered in blooms ranging from pinkish-mauve through almost every imaginable hue of blue. Superior colour forms would be ornamental in gardens in dry regions yet, strangely, have never been introduced into cultivation.

'Agtdaegeneesbos' (eight-day healing bush) is a common name applied to *L. fruticosus* and other lobostemons. This quaint name was coined by early colonists who used an infusion of the leaves to wash body sores and other skin eruptions such as ringworm. The salve was thought to bring about healing within eight days.

LAMIACEAE (LABIATAE)

Mint, sage, thyme and lavender all belong to the large economically important family, the Lamiaceae (or Labiatae as it is alternatively called). However, apart from a few indigenous mints (*Mentha* species), no important culinary herbs are found among the South African representatives, although colourful ornamentals are legion.

In this country the family appears to be centred in the Transvaal. Aromatic foliage and quadrangular stems are obvious identifying characters. Almost every one of the approximately 50 species of *Plectranthus* is worth cultivating. *Plectranthus ecklonii* and *P. fruticosus* are already established garden plants, as is *Leonotis leonurus* — rather confusingly known as wild dagga. Apparently possessing mild narcotic properties but not related to true dagga (*Cannabis*), this splendid garden plant is common in many parts of the country, usually in its orange form. Creamy-white mutations are now also being cultivated.

The diminutive-flowered *Iboza riparia* blooms at the end of winter in a bare, leafless condition, making a most striking display. It is frequent in the Eastern Transvaal and also Natal where the Zulu make infusions of the leaves to cure respiratory complaints.

Pychnostachys urticifolia, notable for its vivid blue flowers, is a tall perennial reaching as much as three metres in height in natural habitat, the North Eastern Transvaal.

341. *Leonotis leonurus:* Wild dagga, Duiwelstabak

342. *Pychnostachys urticifolia*

343. *Plectranthus ecklonii*

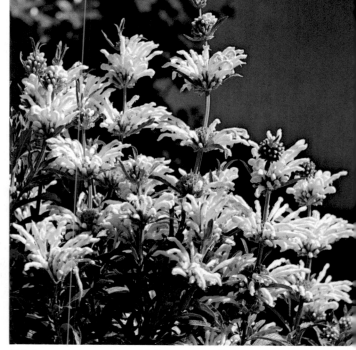

344. *Leonotis leonurus:* Wild dagga, Duiwelstabak

5. Hemizygia foliosa

346. Orthosiphon labiatus

. Plectranthus fruticosus: Muishondblaar

348. Iboza riparia: Iboza, Watersalie

SCROPHULARIACEAE

This large cosmopolitan family has contributed innumerable fine ornamentals to our gardens, many of them South African.

Nemesia strumosa, a multicoloured annual from the Darling sandveld a few kilometres north of Cape Town, is now cultivated worldwide. Despite a very restricted distribution range, there are several naturally occurring colour forms, each peculiar to a specific locality: so plant breeders have had little need to improve on what nature originally provided.

Phygelius capensis, a woody perennial from high cold parts of the Eastern Cape and Drakensberg, is one of the few South African plants sufficiently hardy to thrive outdoors in Britain.

In arid regions, especially the Karoo, various species of *Ap[]simum* are encountered. These small tufted shrublets surv[] long periods of desiccation, but after good spring rains they [] covered with flowers of a quite startlingly vivid blue.

There are also several parasitic genera. *Cycnium adonen[]* from Natal and the Transvaal is a partial parasite, draw[] somewhat on its host's resources but still able to photosynthes[] through its own green leaves. But *Harveya* and *Hyobanche*, bc[] Cape-centred genera, have no green leaves and are total pa[] sites, attached to their hosts' root systems through which th[] draw all their sustenance.

349. *Cycnium adonense:* Mushroom flower

350. *Harveya capensis:* Inkblom

351. *Zaluzianskya* sp.

352. *Nemesia strumosa:* Leeubekkie

. *Nemesia macroceras*

. *Hyobanche sanguinea:* Snail flower, Aardroos

. *Aptosimum depressum:* Wild violet, Brandblare

. *Diascia thunbergiana:* Pensies

357. *Phygelius capensis*

358. *Harveya squamosa*

113

359. *Harveya bolusii:* Inkblom

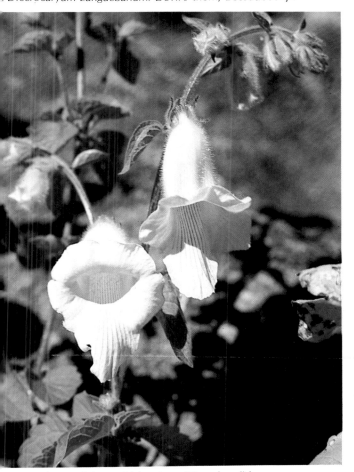

. *Dicerocaryum zanguebarium:* Devil's thorn, Beesdubbeltjie

PEDALIACEAE

The Pedaliaceae is a small family found principally in Africa with a few outliers in Australia and Indo-Malaysia. At least half are indigenous to South Africa.

Sesamum, the largest genus, is well known as a source of oil-rich edible seeds — the popular sesame seeds often seen sprinkled on loaves of bread. Obtained from an Indian species, *S. indicum*, there seems no reason why seeds from any of its approximately 23 indigenous species (especially *S. capense*) should not be equally good if appropriately selected.

Ceratotheca triloba, a common summer-flowering annual in the Transvaal, is often confused with *S. capense*. Both look very much like the foxglove but *Ceratotheca* has sharp spines on the valves of its seed capsule while *Sesamum* does not. This trend towards the development of spines on the seed capsules is very obvious in South African Pedaliaceae; evidently an adaptation to dispersal by animals. *Dicerocaryum zanguebarium*, a trailing creeper from the Transvaal, has stud-like fruits armed with powerful twin spines, like an outsized double-pronged thumbtack. They are picked up on the feet of grazing animals and carried considerable distances.

When immersed in water, the stems and leaves of *Dicerocaryum* give off quantities of soapy mucilage and this species was in fact used as a soap substitute during the Boer War and tribal Africans still use it as a lubricant for women in childbirth.

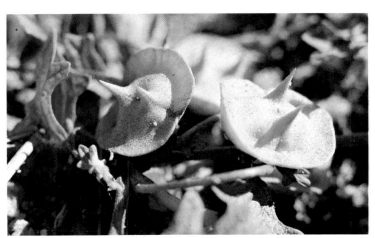

362. *Dicerocaryum zanguebarium:* Devil's thorn, Beesdubbeltjie

. *Ceratotheca triloba:* Wild foxglove, Vingerhoedblom

GESNERIACEAE (STREPTOCARPUS)

Streptocarpus is the only genus of the Gloxinia family in South Africa. Some 45 species are found in our region, mainly in cool, moist, forested parts of the South Eastern Cape, Natal and Transvaal. Nearly all are strikingly beautiful and are much admired as house plants. Species like *S. rexii* and *S. primulifolius* have been extensively used in hybridization programmes to produce more robust floriferous forms. Consequently most hybrids sold both in South Africa and abroad are rather different fr[o] their first cousins in the Natal Midlands.

S. vandeleurii and several related species are remarkable [in] that instead of having a rosette of several leaves, they have [a] single, enormous, rather succulent leaf which supports the ent[ire] plant, including a large cluster of tubular, cream-colour[ed] flowers produced in summer.

363. *Streptocarpus vandeleurii:* Olifantsoor

364. *Streptocarpus primulifolius*

SELAGINACEAE

Some botanists prefer to regard the Selaginaceae as a tribe of the Scrophulariaceae, yet it is in fact a distinct family in which there is a single ovule in each chamber of the ovary instead of several ovules as in true Scrophulariaceae. Most are annuals or soft-wooded perennials. The Selaginaceae is almost exclusively confined to Southern Africa where nine different genera are found with *Selago* the largest, consisting of over 100 species. Several selagos, especially *S. spuria* and *S. serrata*, are exceedingly handsome perennials producing large pinkish to mauve (sometimes white) flowerheads in late spring. At this stage they are little known in gardens but can be expected to generate great interest when eventually introduced into cultivation.

365. *Selago spuria:* Blouaarbossie

366. *Selago spuria:* Blouaarbossie

ACANTHACEAE

he Acanthus family is a large, cosmopolitan group of plants, found in most parts of South Africa
cept the Western Cape. Non-botanists find the Acanthaceae confusingly similar to other related
milies, yet characteristic explosive seed capsules and distinctive sculpturing on their pollen
ains make them readily recognizable. Many such as *Blepharis*, a genus typical of the arid western
rts of the country, have spiny leaves.

Shrubby and herbaceous species of *Barleria* are becoming popular garden plants. The autumn-
wering *B. obtusa* is often used as a ground cover, especially in roadside and embankment plant-
s. Decoctions of the roots of several other *Barleria* species are used by certain African tribes to
ieve toothache.

Of the more woody representatives, *Mackaya bella*, a forest undershrub from Natal, takes well
formal clipping and will flower splendidly in the gloomiest part of a garden where little else will
ive. However, *Ruspolia hypocrateriformis* is not found south of the Soutpansberg: it requires
ly sub-tropical conditions to be cultivated successfully.

368. *Crossandra greenstockii*

7. *Blepharis subvolubilis*

370. *Ruspolia hypocrateriformis*

9. *Barleria gueinzii*

371. *Mackaya bella:* Forest bell bush, Bosklokkiesbos

117

BIGNONIACEAE

South Africa boasts some exceptional members of this largely tropical family. The sausage tree, *Kigelia africana*, could hardly be more appropriately named, yet its singular fruits — which seem to have come straight from a delicatessen's counter — have no gastronomic value. The fruits can in fact be poisonous to man, especially when they are immature, although wild animals are known to eat them. They develop slowly after the rather lurid pendulous blooms have been pollinated. This extraordinary tr grows in the Transvaal Lowveld, Natal and Swaziland.

Tecomaria capensis, the Cape honeysuckle, whose honey-fill tubular flowers are such an attraction to sunbirds, is a promine feature of the Eastern Cape although its range extends to Nat and the Transvaal. An abundance of blooms in orange, yello and salmon-pink, and a multiple-stemmed growth habit ame able to clipping and shaping have ensured its popularity as hedge plant.

On the other hand, *Podranea brycei*, commonly called Zi babwe creeper, is a robust climber liberally festooned w trusses of pink flowers throughout summer. Too rampant for t average gardener, it is nevertheless ideal for those who garden a grand scale.

372. *Kigelia africana:* Sausage tree, Worsboom

373. *Kigelia africana:* Sausage tree, Worsboom

Rhigozum obovatum, com-
nly referred to as the yel-
 pomegranate, is a spare
ggy shrub and is one of the
 members of this family
t has adapted to arid habi-
, such as the central Karoo
 parts of the Eastern Cape.
 much of the year it looks
e dead, but in spring even
 most withered branches
ne to life when the golden
low blossoms make their
ef, brilliant show.

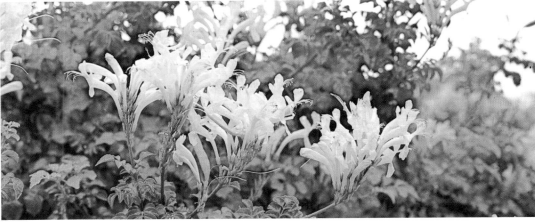

374. *Tecomaria capensis:* Cape honeysuckle, Trompetters

. *Podranea brycei:* Zimbabwe creeper

. *Tecomaria capensis:* Cape honeysuckle, Trompetters

377. *Rhigozum obovatum:* Yellow pomegranate, Berggranaat

119

RUBIACEAE

Gardenias are probably the most familiar members of this huge cosmopolitan family: at least six species are indigenous to South Africa. The much cultivated *Gardenia thunbergia* ranges from the Eastern Cape to Natal. At the end of summer its large, white, deliciously scented blooms are followed by eight centimetre-long oval fruits, hard and woody in texture, which may remain attached to the parent plant for years without releasing their seed. It is believed that these fruits are browsed by kudu or other large ungulates and that their passage through the animal's digestive tract triggers the seeds which then germinate in a bed of dung.

Rothmannia, a related genus of white-flowered evergreen trees, has fruits much favoured by monkeys and baboons.

Pavetta, with about 40 species from the Eastern Cape, Natal

and Transvaal, is also noted for its white, perfumed blooms, b the individual flowers are tightly clustered instead of being p duced singly: moreover, they have slender delicate styles p truding prominently from each flower.

Burchellia bubalina, popularly called wild pomegranate, scentless but produces copious nectar. Birds sometimes te open the tubular flowers to get at the nectar with such det mination that the observant Zulu people have devised for t tree a far more appropriate name, meaning birds' liquor.

The only herbaceous member of the Rubiaceae shown here *Pentanisia prunelloides*, a blue-flowered grassland herb comm in most summer rainfall areas. An infusion of its roots is used several African tribes for treating venereal diseases.

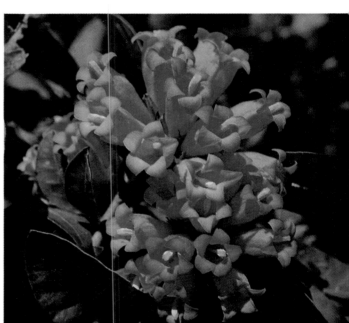

379. *Burchellia bubalina:* Wild pomegranate, Wildegranaat

378. *Gardenia amoena:* Thorny gardenia, Doringkatjiepiering

380. *Rothmannia globosa:* Bell gardenia, Klokkieskatjiepiering

382. *Gardenia thunbergia:* White gardenia. Witkatjiepiering

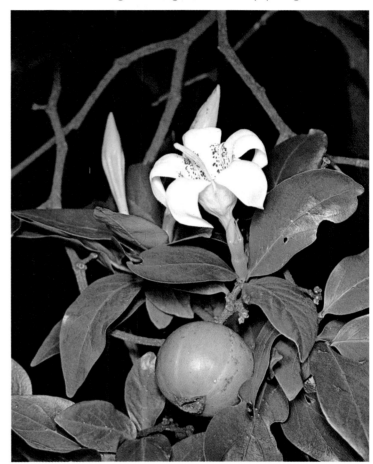

383. *Rothmannia capensis:* Wild gardenia, Wildekatjiepiering

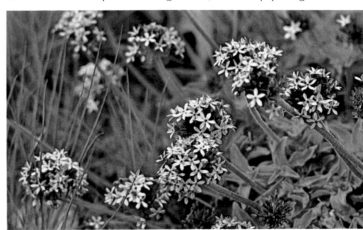

384. *Pentanisia prunelloides:* Wild verbena

. *Pavetta breyeri*

121

ASTERACEAE
(COMPOSITAE)

The Asteraceae (alternatively called Compositae) is known to everyone as the daisy family. Comprising some 25 000 species distributed throughout the world, it is one of the largest families of flowering plants. They are considered advanced in evolutionary terms and are certainly one of the most successful plant groups, having adapted to almost every ecological niche and assumed almost every growth form imaginable. Well over 2 000 species are found in South Africa. An important family feature is that each so-called daisy blossom is actually a compound flower-head, usually comprised of numerous tiny individual flowers e circled by brightly coloured rays.

Many are important ornamentals such as gerberas, the mo widely cultivated of our native daisies. Modern *Gerbera* hybri are mainly derived from *Gerbera jamesonii*, the Barberton dai of the Eastern Transvaal, and *G. aurantiaca*, the Hilton daisy fro central Natal.

Spring at the Cape would be inconceivable without daisies li *Didelta carnosa* which so often features in the foreground

385. *Didelta carnosa*

122

ture-postcard views of Table Mountain, together with other ie species like *Senecio arenarius* and *S. littoreus*.

verlastings is a general term for various species of *Heli-ysum, Helipterum* and *Phaenocoma*, whose dry papery rays sist, retaining their colour for years: they are collected from veld in great quantities for dry arrangements. In the Southern ie districts of Elim and Bredasdorp, *Helichrysum vestitum* e formed the basis of an unusual local industry. Detached ids of this aromatic white-flowered everlasting were plucked,

dried and then used for stuffing pillows, from whose pungent, herbal petal filling it was claimed that asthmatic sleepers derived considerable relief.

Daisies are so ubiquitous that they are considered common, yet some species like *Senecio coleophyllus*, a tall swamp dweller from the Cape Hangklip Mountains, are exceedingly rare. Others such as *Mairea coriacea* only flower immediately after a veld fire and so at other times are passed unnoticed.

Gazania, Gorteria, Dimorphotheca, Felicia, Senecio and *Ursinia*

Gerbera aurantiaca: Hilton daisy

388. *Felicia amoena*

Senecio arenarius (purple): Hongerblom

389. *Helichrysum sesamoides:* Everlasting, Sewejaartjie

123

390. *Senecio tamoides*.

393. *Senecio coleophyllus*

391. *Gazania krebsiana*: Oranjegousblom

394. *Dimorphotheca cuneata*: Gousblom

392. *Helichrysum vestitum:*
Cape everlasting, Sewejaartjie

395. *Phaenocoma prolifera*: Cape everlasting, Rooisewejaartjie

contribute to the famed spring daisy displays in Namaqua-
~~l~~d. They are mostly annuals germinating in response to early
~~a~~umn rains, growing throughout winter and then flowering in
~~spr~~ing, after which they rapidly set seed and die as summer ad-
~~van~~ces. Not every year sees carpets of daisies in Namaqualand,

for the volume and regularity of winter rainfall determines the
extent of the show: weather conditions in this area are so erratic
that one can rarely expect a bumper season more than once a
decade.

Another colourful genus in semi-arid regions is *Euryops*, com-

Gorteria diffusa var. calendulacea

398. *Mairea coriacea*

Helipterum eximium: Cape everlasting, Rooisewejaartjie

399. *Euryops brevilobus*

125

400. *Ursinia anthemoides:* Marigold, Bergmargriet

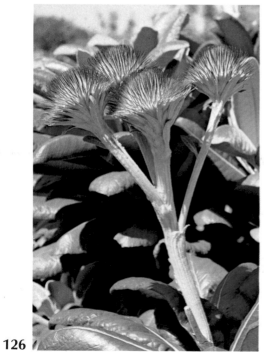

401. *Oldenburgia arbuscula:*
Suurberg cushion bush, Suurbergse kussingbos

402. *Helipterum canescens:*
Everlasting, Rooisewejaartjie

403. *Dicoma zeyheri:* Maagwortel

Felicia filifolia: Draaibossie

monly called 'harpuisbos' because of resinous exudations from both stems and leaves. Comprising quick-growing evergreen shrubs, some species such as *E. speciosissimus*, the Clanwilliam daisy, have become popular garden ornamentals.

Woody, perennial species tend to predominate in the moister eastern half of the country. Several are creepers like *Senecio tamoides*, a yellow winter-flowering species which grows wild near Humansdorp. Around Grahamstown, *Oldenburgia arbuscula* develops into a most arresting small tree, producing gigantic thistle-like flowerheads on metre-long stems.

Helichrysum ecklonis

BIBLIOGRAPHY

The following reference works will provide detailed information on specific aspects of South Africa's wild flowers.

Regional Guides

CAPE PROVINCE
Adams, J. (1976) *Wild Flowers of the Northern Cape,* Dept. of Nature and Environmental Conservation, Cape Provincial Administration.

Batten, A. & Bokelmann, H. (1966) *Wild Flowers of the Eastern Cape Province,* Books of Africa, Cape Town.

Eliovson, S. (1972) *Namaqualand in Flower,* Macmillan, Johannesburg.

Gledhill, E. (1969) *Eastern Cape Veld Flowers,* Dept. of Nature and Environmental Conservation, Cape Provincial Administration.

Hobson, N. K., Jessop, J. P., Gihn, M. C. & Kelly, J. (1975) *Veld Plants of Southern Africa* (mainly Karoo region), Macmillan, Johannesburg.

Kidd, M. M. (1973) *Wild Flowers of the Cape Peninsula,* Oxford University Press, Cape Town.

Luckhoff, C. A. (1951) *Table Mountain,* A. A. Balkema, Cape Town.

Mason, H. (1972) *Western Cape Sandveld Flowers,* C. Struik, Cape Town.

NATAL
Gibson, J. M. (1975) *Wild Flowers of Natal (coastal region),* Trustees of the Natal Publishing Trust Fund, Durban.

Gibson, J. M. (1978) *Wild Flowers of Natal (inland region),* Trustees of the Natal Publishing Trust Fund, Durban.

Jeppe, B. (1975) *Natal Wild Flowers,* Purnell & Sons, Johannesburg.

Pearse, R. O. (1978) *Mountain Splendour: The Wild Flowers of the Drakensberg,* Howard Timmins, Cape Town.

Trauseld, W. P. (1969) *Wild Flowers of the Natal Drakensberg,* Purnell & Sons, Johannesburg.

TRANSVAAL
Jeppe, B. (illus. by) (1964) *Trees and Shrubs of the Witwatersrand,* Witwatersrand University Press, Johannesburg.

Letty, C. (1962) *Wild Flowers of the Transvaal,* Trustees Wildflowers of the Transvaal Book Fund, Pretoria.

Lucas, A. & Pike, B. (1971) *Wild Flowers of the Witwatersrand,* Purnell & Sons, Johannesburg.

Van Wyk, P. (1972 and 1974) *Trees of the Kruger National Park,* vols. 1 & 2, Purnell & Sons, Johannesburg.

Allied Topics of Interest

TREES (general)
Coates Palgrave, P. (1977) *Trees of Southern Africa,* C. Struik, Cape Town.

Palmer, E. & Pitman, N. (1973) *Trees of Southern Africa,* 3 vols., A. A. Balkema, Cape Town.

VELD TYPES
Acocks, J. P. H. (1975) *Veld Types of South Africa* (2nd ed.), Botanical Survey Memoir No. 40, Government Printer, Pretoria. (Available at R6,00 from Division of Agricultural Information, Private Bag X144, Pretoria.)

FOLKLORE AND MEDICINAL USES
Smith, C. A. (1966) *Common Names of South African Plants,* Botanical Survey Memoir No. 35, Agricultural Technical Services, Pretoria.

Watt, J. M. & Breyer-Brankdwijk, M. G. (1962) *Medicinal and Poisonous Plants of Southern and Eastern Africa* (2nd ed.), E. S. Livingstone, Edinburgh and London.

Detailed Publications

ASCLEPIADACEAE
White, A. & Sloane, B. L. (1973) *The Stapeliae* (3 vols.), Abbey Gard Press, Pasadena, California.

ERICACEAE
Baker, H. A. & Oliver, E. G. (1967) *Ericas in Southern Africa,* Purnel Sons, Johannesburg.

EUPHORBIACEAE
White, A., Dyer, R. A. & Sloane, B. L. (1941) *The Succulent Euphorbiace* 2 vols., Abbey Garden Press, Pasadena, California.

FABACEAE
Carr, J. D. (1976) *The South African Acacias,* Conservation Press, Joh nesburg.

Hennessy, E. F. (1972) *South African Erythrinas,* Natal Branch of the W life Protection Society, Durban.

GERANIACEAE
Van der Walt, J. J. A. (1977) *Pelargoniums of Southern Africa,* illus. Ellaphie Ward-Hilhorst, Purnell & Sons, Johannesburg.

GESNERIACEAE
Hilliard, O. M. & Burtt, B. L. (1971) *Streptocarpus: An African Plant Stu* Natal University Press, Pietermaritzburg.

IRIDACEAE
Delpierre, G. R. & Du Plessis, N. M. (1974) *The Winter-growing Gladiol* South Africa, Tafelberg, Cape Town.

Lewis, G. J., Obermeyer, A. A. & Barnard, T. J.: 'A Revision of the So African species of Gladiolus,' *Journal of South African Botany,* sup vol. No. 10, 1972.

LILIACEAE
Bornman, H. & Hardy, D. (1971) *Aloes of the South African Veld,* Voortr ker Pers, Johannesburg.

Jeppe, B. (1969) *South African Aloes,* Purnell & Sons, Johannesburg.

Leighton, F. M.: 'The Genus Agapanthus,' *Journal of South African Bota* suppl. vol. no. 4 (1965).

Reynolds, G. W. (1950) *Aloes of South Africa,* Aloes of South Africa Bo Fund, Johannesburg.

MESEMBRYANTHEMACEAE
Herre, H. (1971) *The Genera of the Mesembryanthemaceae,* Tafelbe Cape Town.

Sprechmann, D. L. (1970) *Lithops,* Fairleigh Dickinson University Pre United States of America.

ORCHIDACEAE
Harrison, E. R. (1972) *Epiphytic Orchids of Southern Africa,* Natal Brar of the Wildlife Protection Society, Durban.

Schelpe, E. A. (1966) *An Introduction to South African Orchids,* Purr & Sons, Johannesburg.

PROTEACEAE
Rourke, J. P. (1980) *The Proteas of Southern Africa,* Purnell & Sons, Joh nesburg.